THE PERFECT GIFT

THE PERFECT GIFT

A Collection of Heartwarming True Christmas Stories

A. L. SOWARDS • ANITA STANSFIELD • BREANNA OLAVESON
ELLEN FAY BELNAP • GANEL-LYN CONDIE • JENNIFER MOORE
KRISTA LYNNE JENSEN • MEG JOHNSON • MELANIE JACOBSON
PAMELA CARRINGTON REID • SANDRA GREY • SIAN ANN BESSEY

Covenant Communications, Inc.

Cover image: *Christmas Gift with Evergreen Garland* © Catherine Lane, courtesy istockphoto.com

Published by Covenant Communications, Inc.
American Fork, Utah

Printed in the United States of America
First Printing: October 2016

10 9 8 7 6 5 4 3 2

ISBN 978-1-52440-119-1

A CHRISTMAS REROUTE

BY A. L. SOWARDS

Names have been changed, and details have been filled in when memories were fuzzy, but the following is a true story. Thank you to my dear friends "Bethany," "Sue," and "Bob" for allowing me to share it.

December 1999

Santa Claus had it easy. Bethany was sure slipping down a narrow chimney was less of a logistics challenge than changing a newborn's diaper in an airplane lavatory while a toddler yanked on her Christmas sweater.

She washed her hands and strapped baby Marina back in the borrowed baby carrier, then took her son's hand and escaped from the confines of the lavatory into the Boeing 727's center aisle.

"See Grandma and Grandpa now?" Ralphie asked.

"Not yet. But we're almost there." Bethany collapsed into her seat, counting down the minutes until she could see her parents again. Flying with two kids was exhausting even without any hiccups, and so far this trip was about as smooth as the rocky-road fudge her school principal made every December.

Her original flight from Salt Lake to Denver had been cancelled. She'd been fortunate enough to get another direct flight only a few hours later, but waiting in line for her new assignment and then getting both kids to a different terminal had made her tired before they'd even boarded. So far, Ralphie and Marina had been good, but the constant worry that one of them would start crying was draining Bethany's remaining energy.

As the pilot announced their descent, a passenger across the aisle smiled at Marina. "Cute baby."

"Thank you." Bethany ran her fingers over her daughter's fuzzy head and down her newborn-soft cheeks.

"How old is she?"

"Almost six weeks."

"Oh." The woman's eyebrows lifted in surprise. Her lips tightened as if biting back a remark about how that was too early to take a baby on an airplane. She straightened her scarf decorated with metallic snowflakes and turned to speak with a different passenger.

Six weeks was young, but her doctor had cleared this trip, and Bethany didn't want to spend Christmas alone.

She wouldn't have been completely alone in Utah. She had her kids. And her sister-in-law would have made time to do something together, just like she'd made time to drive Bethany to the airport that morning. Bethany wasn't sure she could still refer to Lindsey as her sister-in-law. Bethany's divorce wasn't finalized, but her marriage to Lindsey's brother was broken. Staying in Utah sounded like a sure route to a blue Christmas.

As their airplane taxied to the gate, Bethany put away Ralphie's books and handed him his Spider-Man action figure. The shuffle off the plane was crowded and slow. Ralphie lifted his arms like he wanted to be held, but she wasn't supposed to lift anything heavier than Marina for a few more weeks.

"Grandpa will carry you in a few minutes." She offered her hand, and Ralphie took it, content for the moment.

When she reached the gate, she looked around for her parents. Her dad's height usually made him easy to spot, but she couldn't see him. Marina was acting hungry again, and Ralphie needed a break after being cooped up in the plane. "Let's go for a little walk."

Her parents weren't at any of the nearby gates. Maybe they'd been held up in traffic, or maybe the security line was long. She'd left a message for them about her cancelled flight before leaving the Salt Lake airport, but what if they hadn't gotten it?

"Where's Grandma and Grandpa?" Ralphie asked.

"Let's find a chair and give your sister some food. I bet they'll be here soon." But even after she fed and burped the baby and gave her a new diaper, Bethany's parents were nowhere to be seen.

She'd come in on a different airline, but surely Delta could tell her parents her new United itinerary. She was tempted to go to baggage claim, but they'd promised to meet at the gate, and she wasn't sure Ralphie could trek that far without a meltdown. His little legs had already walked more that day than a Walmart employee's on Black Friday. Terminal B was enormous. If she wandered too far from where she'd arrived, her parents really wouldn't be able to find her. She needed to stay near her arrival gate.

"Mom, I'm thirsty."

Bethany gave Ralphie a Capri Sun and dragged him to another line—their fourth of the day. She bounced lightly back and forth, trying to keep Marina happy. Ralphie finished his drink and handed her the garbage. She put it in the diaper bag and reached for his hand, but he pulled away.

"Ralphie, stay with Mommy."

He looked at the bright lights of the nearest food kiosk and took a few steps toward it.

"Ralphie, where's Spider-Man?" She found his action figure and shook it until he came and got it. While they waited, she rummaged through her bag. She'd packed light to give her recovering abdomen a break, and now she was running out of bribery material. She had a few more Goldfish crackers and a bag of fruit snacks. After that, she'd be in trouble.

* * *

Sue Gardner felt as if she'd been waiting in line long enough to have listened to an unabridged performance of Handel's *Messiah.* "I wonder where they are."

Bob, her husband and mission companion, glanced at his watch, then at the line for the Delta counter. "We should find out soon."

Sue was eager to snuggle her grandchildren. And she wanted to make this an easy trip for Bethany. Bags of diapers and canisters of formula waited in their apartment, and they'd given themselves extra time to get to the airport so Bethany wouldn't have to carry anything heavier than the baby. Finding the gate deserted had been an unpleasant surprise. She was starting to get worried.

Her concern over Bethany had been churning for months, ever since her former son-in-law's shocking announcement that he was done with the Church and done with fatherhood. In a matter of months, Bethany had gone from being the mother of one with a super-dad husband to a mother of two with an absent husband. Sue was happy to be on a mission, but being in Denver made it harder to help Bethany.

They finally reached the front of the line and explained the situation to the agent at the counter.

"Yes, I see that flight was cancelled," the agent said.

"So is she coming in tomorrow instead? Is she on a later flight?" Sue looked at the clock hanging behind the counter. They'd been in line for nearly an hour.

The agent shrugged.

"Can you find out?"

The agent picked up the phone and talked for a few minutes before hanging up again. "All the passengers were reassigned. She's not listed on our later flight. She might be on a different airline."

"So where would she come in?"

The Delta agent shrugged again.

"Can you page her?" Bob asked.

They waited for a while, then finally heard the loudspeaker blaring around Terminal C, "Bethany Sandhurst to the nearest courtesy phone please, Bethany Sandhurst to the nearest courtesy phone."

* * *

"Bob and Sue Gardner to the nearest courtesy phone please, Bob and Sue Gardner . . ." The intercom went silent, and Bethany crossed her fingers. But no one came, and the minutes stretched into an hour. Even after feeding Marina another bottle, there was no news from the United counter.

"Can you tell me where I would have come in if my first flight hadn't been cancelled?"

"I don't know. Sorry." The United rep turned to the next person in line.

Ralphie had sat down on the carpet, and he didn't want to get up again. His big eyes drooped, and his lips turned down in a pout. He was tired.

Bethany spotted a row of baggage carts for rent. "Want a ride, Ralphie?"

His eyes lit up when he saw where she was pointing. She slipped the coins in the slots and released a cart.

She hated spending the money. Her house was on the market, but it hadn't sold. Making the mortgage payments had been manageable with two incomes, but since her husband left, house payments had absorbed most of her paycheck and eaten away at her savings. Add in medical bills from the baby and a few Christmas presents, and she was broke. She had to watch every penny.

Even though she wasn't supposed to lift him, she picked Ralphie up to get him in the carry-on slot. It wasn't designed as a child seat, but she couldn't carry him. Even that brief lift made her C-section incision burn.

She pushed the cart to a payphone and called her parents' toll-free number. Maybe one of them had stayed at the apartment. Or maybe they could check their messages from a payphone. She chuckled at that. Her parents were more likely to get run over by a reindeer than accomplish something as technologically savvy as retrieving messages remotely. They didn't pick up the phone, but she left a message anyway. "It's Bethany. I flew in on United, and I'm in Terminal B, Gate 43."

She hung up the phone and leaned her forehead against the booth. She debated trying another terminal. But the Denver airport had trams from terminal to terminal, and they didn't allow baggage carts on the trams. She didn't have enough cash to pay for a new one at each terminal. Not for the first time that afternoon, she offered a silent prayer. *Please let them find me.*

* * *

Sue looked at her watch again. They'd been in the airport for three hours. They'd paged Bethany twice, asked four service reps for help, wandered through baggage claim and a dozen concourses, and they still couldn't find their daughter and grandchildren.

"Do you think she called us?" Bob asked.

"Probably." Not that it mattered. Sue didn't know how to check the messages unless she was home to push play.

Bob walked over to a payphone, and Sue followed. "Who are you calling?"

"Our apartment."

"Why?"

"To check the messages."

"You know how to do that?"

* * *

Bethany read the same book to Ralphie for the sixth time. He was usually good at listening to stories—better than some of her kindergarteners—but his attention was waning.

He pushed the book away. "I'm hungry."

Bethany pulled out the last bag of fruit snacks.

Ralphie finished it in less than a minute. "More?"

She dug through the diaper bag again and couldn't find anything. There were places to eat in the airport, but airport food was notoriously expensive. She could put it on her credit card if she had to, but she kept hoping her parents would appear. "Let's go on another walk and look for Grandma and Grandpa."

They'd made it past only a few gates when Marina woke up. A few more gates, and her fussing grew to a thin newborn wail. Bethany looked at her watch. The baby was probably hungry again. She washed one of the used bottles out in the drinking fountain and had Ralphie hold it while she took out the formula container. She'd packed three times what she'd thought she would need, but this bottle would use the last of it, and then she'd have maybe two hours. She felt a dread similar to what she felt every January when it was time to take the Christmas lights off the house—only this wasn't a countdown to scraped knuckles and frozen fingers. This was worse. This was a countdown to a hungry baby with no food.

"See how many airplanes you can find," she told Ralphie as she pushed the baggage cart up to a window. The flash of lights from carts pulling piles of luggage distracted him for a minute or two. Long enough for Bethany to get her tears under control.

She didn't want to cry, but she'd been on the verge of tears for hours. She'd lost track of the number of times she'd waited in line to talk to an airline rep, only to have them brush her off or tell her they simply didn't know how to help. Was she ever going to get out of the airport? With the divorce proceedings, she'd felt stuck for months, figuratively, but now that feeling was literal. She needed help. Worse, her kids needed help. Hot tears rolled down her cheeks, and she brushed them away with her shoulders because she had the baby in one hand and the bottle in the other.

She'd tried so hard to be a good wife. Her marriage had fallen apart anyway. Now she was trying so hard to be a good mother, and she couldn't even get her kids from Salt Lake to Denver without disaster. She'd done everything she could think of. What else was she supposed to do?

Marina finished her bottle and continued sucking on the collapsed nipple like she wanted more. Bethany didn't have any more to give her. She burped the baby and got her to take a pacifier. She didn't know what she was supposed to do next. She couldn't afford the taxi fare to her parents' apartment, couldn't afford a rental car. Couldn't even afford chicken nuggets for her hungry little boy.

"Grandpa!" Ralphie almost bolted from the cart.

Bethany whipped her head around, and she was instantly crying again. Her parents had finally found her.

* * *

Sue held her granddaughter as they took the tram to baggage claim. She kissed the top of Marina's head and inhaled that sweet newborn smell. She put her free hand on Bethany's arm. "I'm sorry it took us so long, sweetie. We didn't realize the paging system just worked on Terminal C, not on the whole airport."

"I didn't know Dad could check the answering machine from a payphone. I'm impressed." Bethany seemed tired but content.

Ralphie watched the tunnel flash past through the tram windows. Sue had bought him a hamburger, and he was full of energy again. It was a rough start, but she was going to make sure it was a good trip from here on out.

But when they got to baggage claim, the car seats were missing. They looked around all the baggage carousels, at the oversized luggage claim, and in the lost-luggage room.

Bob sighed. "We'll drive slow and stop to get some at the nearest Walmart."

Bethany shook her head. "I'm not taking a newborn in a car without a car seat."

Bob went to wait in yet another line to talk to yet another airport rep. Sue did her best to put on a happy face, but she was discouraged. Hadn't this day been rough enough?

After another forty-five minutes of asking, waiting, and walking around baggage claim, Sue thought Bob's idea was sounding better and better. After using up the last size-one diaper, she was certain. "Let's get out of this airport, sweetie."

"You don't have any diapers in the car, do you?"

"Just at the apartment."

Bethany took another look at the baggage carousel and nodded. "Yeah, let's go."

As they headed for the door, an airport worker walked from a side room with two car seats. "We just found these. Are they yours?"

"Yes." Bethany's eyes lifted upward as if in prayer. Santa himself couldn't have made a more longed-for delivery.

* * *

On Christmas Eve, Bethany snuggled with Marina while her father read the Christmas story from the Bible. Her parents' apartment didn't look much like Christmas. The decorations she remembered from childhood were all in storage. There wasn't even a Christmas tree. But Christmas wasn't about ornaments or stockings.

She had tried to make things special in the weeks before her trip for Ralphie's sake, but none of the glittering decorations had made it seem like Christmas to her. Now, with nothing but a single garland to mark the season, she felt surrounded by the spirit of Christmas. It was in the gentle peace she felt as her father read from Luke, in the sweet Christmas carols her mother sang to Marina, and in the cheerful well-wishes from the owners of the Italian restaurant where they'd eaten that night.

Ralphie squealed with delight as his grandpa tickled him. "Come on, squirt." Her dad held out his hand and took Ralphie off to bed.

Bethany laughed when she heard them singing "Jingle Bells" a few minutes later. "He just learned that song."

"He's a smart kid," Bethany's mom said as she fed Marina a bottle. "You're doing a good job with him."

"Sometimes I wonder."

"Sweetie, you've had a rough year. But you are a great mom. You've been a great mom since day one. Don't you remember how tough you were when Ralphie was born?"

"You don't forget a trip like that." She winced at the memory of driving down Utah's potholed freeway the day after her C-section to visit her newborn baby boy at Primary Children's Hospital. Marina's C-section had been so much easier physically—but it had been alone, and that had made it harder in a lot of other ways.

"You do wonders in the classroom every year. Half those kids don't even know how to open a book when you get them, and by the end of the year, they're reading as well as first graders. You do amazing things with them. And you're doing amazing things with your kids."

After her parents went to bed, Bethany thought long and hard. Since the divorce, she'd been getting through one day at a time. First she'd had a new school year to plan, then she'd had a newborn to take care of. She'd been surviving from one day to the next, rarely thinking beyond the next task. And that wasn't how she wanted to live her life.

Buoyed up by her mother's encouragement, she leafed through the scriptures sitting on the end table next to the couch. She flipped to Matthew and read about the Wise Men, then about Mary and Joseph fleeing into Egypt. Mary must have been so scared. But God had protected little Jesus and His parents. They'd had to do the actual traveling, but God had given them the warning they'd needed.

Bethany sat completely still, pondering the story. She hadn't had a lot of time for reflection lately—she'd been too busy, too sleep-deprived, too worried. But now she recognized what she needed to know, her Christmas message from her loving Heavenly Father. She needed to do her part, but what she couldn't do, she could leave to her Savior. He would be with her every step of the way.

Before she went to sleep she checked on Marina and Ralphie. Marina lay with her hands stretched above her head. Her round cheeks looked as cherubic as the angels gracing some of her parents' Christmas cards. Ralphie was snuggled under a blanket, no doubt with visions of sugar plums dancing in his head. Bethany smiled. Her children's future—her future—still looked challenging. But now that challenge was illuminated with hope.

* * *

The smell of roasting turkey filled the kitchen. Sue chopped the last potato and dropped it in the pot of water as Christmas carols rang from the CD player. She dried her hands and ate a piece of toffee to tide her over until it was time for their Christmas feast.

"Do you have any hot chocolate?" Bethany asked when she came back from putting the baby down for a nap.

Sue grabbed some from the cupboard. "We've got milk chocolate, raspberry, and peppermint."

"Good, because if Dad and Ralphie stay outside much longer, they're going to need it. Ralphie loves the snow, but it's been too cold for Marina, so I haven't taken him out much this year."

Sue walked over to the window. The snowman Bob and Ralphie were building was just about finished. Bob took his newsboy-style hat and put it on top. Ralphie clapped in delight.

"They still need a face." Sue dug through the fridge and found a baby carrot for the nose. But what about the eyes? A bowl of candies collected from their stockings that morning sat on the countertop. She grabbed two mini Snickers and put on her coat. Bethany followed her outside.

"Grandma!" Ralphie grinned when he saw her. "Look what we made, Mom!"

Sue handed him the carrot and unwrapped the candy bars for him. Bob and Bethany smiled along with her as Ralphie placed the eyes, one slightly higher than the other. Sue had wanted to give Ralphie a special Christmas, and she had wanted to help Bethany. Looking at them laughing together, she thought she was succeeding. And by focusing on others, she and Bob had created a magical Christmas for themselves.

* * *

Two weeks after arriving, Bethany was back at the Denver airport, hugging her parents good-bye. "Thank you for everything. I had a great trip. Once we finally got here."

"We had fun too," her mom said. "I can't remember a better Christmas. After we got past that rocky start."

Her dad set Ralphie on the ground and handed him his favorite Christmas present, a soft stuffed antelope. "Bye, squirt. Be a good boy."

Bethany took her son's hand and rubbed Marina's back through the baby carrier. She was starting to get a little fussy, but as soon as they were seated, Bethany could make her a bottle. Ralphie waved at his grandparents and wrapped an arm around his toy before skipping along beside her.

As she carried her daughter and guided her son, Bethany realized she was on her own again for the first time in two weeks. She winced internally, but the apprehension quickly passed. Her parents would stay until the plane took off, and her sister-in-law, or ex-sister-in-law, would be there to pick her up in Salt Lake. Bethany had survived the trip from Salt Lake to Denver, and she figured if she could handle that, she could handle just about anything.

Christmas had been good for her, and not because of the nice gifts or the good food or the funny Christmas movies. This Christmas had been about hope. The hope that came with a newborn Savior and hope for her family's future. Soon would come the normal routine of taking care of her children and teaching her students, but Bethany had confidence she could handle it better than she had in the past. Being a single, working mother wasn't her first choice, but she placed her trust in the Savior, knowing He would help her whenever she fell short.

OTHER BOOKS BY A. L. SOWARDS

Deadly Alliance

Sworn Enemy

Espionage

The Rules in Rome

The Spider and the Sparrow

PRECIOUS MOMENTS

BY ANITA STANSFIELD

As this last Christmas approached, I found myself, not for the first time, feeling somewhat Grinchy, or maybe it was Scroogey. Although I must interject that both Scrooge's and the Grinch's stories are about a dramatic change of heart, so perhaps it's unfair to always use their names, fictional though they may be, to describe negative and cynical attitudes toward the greatest of all holidays. The Grinch's small heart grew enormously on that momentous Christmas morning after he'd attempted to steal all the things he'd believed were necessary for a happy Christmas celebration, and it's declared at the conclusion of *A Christmas Carol* that "Scrooge was better than his word . . . and it was always said of him that he knew how to keep Christmas well."

Given these facts, let me clarify that I was feeling almost as bad as the Grinch and Scrooge felt *prior* to their miraculous change of heart—though my negativity was not nearly so severe. I love Christmas and was sincerely committed to keeping it well; however, with ongoing health issues and financial challenges, Christmas, for all my efforts to always keep the true meaning in its proper place, had come to feel overwhelming in many respects.

Early in the course of my being a mother and being in charge of Christmas celebrations in our home, I came to realize that for all of my best efforts, I could never measure up to the standard my own sweet mother had set for how Christmas should be. Of course, as a child you never see the clues of how much work a mother is putting into such things, but in looking back and assembling the pieces of my memories, I could see that my parents had put a high priority on making Christmas as perfect as possible for their children, and my mother—being the homemaker—had put in an enormous amount of work. There had never been extravagant or expensive gifts, but there had always been an abundance of many things to open on Christmas morning. I also realized in looking back that my mother had used Christmas as an excuse to put the house in near perfect order. Spring cleaning was nothing compared to my mother's cleaning preparations for Christmas. I doubt my room was ever cleaner or more in order than it was on Christmas Eve, including clean sheets on the bed that added to the magical effect of trying to go to sleep wearing brand-new pajamas.

My mother also put a great deal of effort into making a certain amount of Christmas goodies that seemed mandatory. The aromas and tastes of the foods associated with Christmas are still vivid in my memory. I can't dispute that with all things combined, my mother certainly knew how to make Christmas feel magical and idyllic, though I know now that she was also frazzled and tired, and perhaps if she had it to do over again, she might not have spent as much time cleaning and cooking. And it would have been all right.

I personally let go of trying to make those same memories many years ago. I minimized and pared down little by little as our family became larger and my career became more complicated. Still, I always managed to create a good Christmas for my family, and it was something I always found fulfilling and worth the effort.

And I always seek to keep Christ at the center of Christmas and feel strongly about the essence of certain facets of our celebrations contributing to the intended spirit of the holiday. Like most things in this world, putting up lights and decorating trees and singing songs and watching tender movies and giving gifts to those we love can all be good if they're done with proper intentions.

I love the feel of the house with the Christmas tree properly lit and adorned, and I love getting gifts for my loved ones and seeing them wrapped and accumulating beneath the tree. I love the music and the movies, and I love it when I feel glimpses of that tender warmth inside of me that reminds me of my own childhood Christmases and, more importantly, of the Spirit of Christ.

Nevertheless, in spite of all that, chronic illness and subsequent financial struggles have made the approach of Christmas the last few years difficult to face. It has come to feel overwhelming and exhausting, and I've found it increasingly necessary to talk myself into being positive and making the most of it—for the sake of my children and grandchildren, if nothing else.

Nevertheless, I've sought for a cure to my anti-Christmas blues the same way I always have—even if it has become increasingly difficult through the years. I've watched Christmas movies to pass the time while I've been too ill to get out of bed, and I've saturated myself with the Christmas music I love. I've learned the benefit of online shopping and how economical it can be when I can manage to get free shipping. If not for this blessing of the twenty-first century, I couldn't do my own Christmas shopping at all.

My daughters love Christmas and are wonderful at overseeing the decorating and gift wrapping and whatever else needs to be physically done in order to pull Christmas together now. Without them, I fear the holiday would be a sore disappointment. But it all seems to come together on Christmas Eve when my married children come with their families and we're all together for a wonderful meal, the exchanging of gifts, and just being together. I know this part of the holiday means a great deal to all of them, and it's something I hope will hold fast in their memories throughout their lives as they face their own challenges.

Yes, it all comes together and usually rather well in spite of my concerns leading up to the big event.

Except when it doesn't.

This Christmas I couldn't get my mind away from all of the difficulties that had marred Christmas celebrations in recent years. There had been illness and surgery and cancer and bad moods and contention and foul weather—just to name the forerunners on the list. I prayed every day for the absence of all these things in our forthcoming Christmas celebration, needing to feel like my efforts would all be worth it and that we could share a good Christmas together as a family.

But a week or so before Christmas, it occurred to me that—as I've heard many times—the most constant thing in life is change. More specifically, a family is always in a state of flux. When my children were little, I had more control over Christmas and how it all played out. We all lived under the same roof, and even though challenges came up and glitches occurred, I felt more in control in dealing with them. Now three of my five children are married, and I have gained three precious new daughters who are my son's wives. Grandchildren are coming into the family and growing and changing continually. The dynamics of my children's lives have changed and are affected by all these things, just as dynamics change with every family.

The bottom line is that I think I finally accepted that I do *not* have control over whether or not it will all come together and work out as a pleasant experience. And just as with many lessons I have learned in life, I recognized that what applies to Christmas applies to the rest of my experiences in this existence: I can do only what I'm capable of doing. I can be grateful for the assistance and support of others. I can strive to keep my priorities in the right place. And then I just have to let go and give it to God, and by letting go, I mean really letting go of my expectation of the outcome. If the weather or germs or cancer or disagreements create challenges, there's always another day, another year, another Christmas in the future. And in the whole grand scheme of things, the disappointments and difficulties may not be as bad as they feel in the moment.

With my determination firmly set on pulling everything together with the help of my daughters, both of whom I believe secretly acquired skills at the North Pole while I wasn't looking, I pressed forward through the days of December, thrilled that we would have a white Christmas. I never want snow to make travel difficult for anyone, but, oh, how I love the atmosphere it creates!

My husband and I did what we'd recently made a tradition—we sat on the bed in our pajamas with a laptop and ordered Christmas gifts for every member of the family. Our budget was limited, but we found on their wish lists inexpensive items we knew they wanted, and as the packages arrived and we wrapped them, I felt an anticipation over the potential excitement—especially with the young children.

When Christmas Eve arrived, no one was sick, and I was still filled with that pleasant anticipation. The roads were clear for travel, but the snow on the ground and trees was beautiful, and so far everything was under control. I was greatly looking forward to a nice meal with my entire family and the excitement of my children as they exchanged their sibling gifts and the joy of my grandchildren, who would get to open one of their gifts from Grammy and Pop. And all but one were old enough to be terribly impatient to get dinner over with and get to the good part.

When dinner was finally cleaned up, we all gathered to exchange gifts. It was tradition for the youngest to go first. Evy had been born in July and didn't have a personal interest in her gift, but her parents were pleased. Next came Smith, who was almost two. Now, getting a gift for Smith had been a conundrum. The child was obsessed with balls—anything and everything round. His parents had told us they'd gotten him toys that all were related to balls, so what could we give him that he would like that we could afford? He had little to no interest in cars or dinosaurs or other things his father and uncles had liked at that age. We'd searched online and come down to a classic red rubber dodge ball—the kind we all used in elementary school. The ball had arrived in its deflated form, and my husband had filled it with air before I'd put it into a large gift bag with tissue paper to cover it.

I always watch closely to see the reactions of my loved ones when they open gifts. I want them to not only like what's been chosen for them but to also feel the love meant to come with the gift. But I felt a special anticipation with Smith's red ball. His father pulled the pieces of tissue paper out of the bag like a magician pulling scarves out of his sleeve. Then Smith's big brown eyes *popped.* I don't use that word lightly. He's a child, not a cartoon character, but when he saw that big red ball, his eyes *popped.* He pulled it out of the bag, squealing with delight and hugging the ball with arms that couldn't reach all the way around it, and then he did a true, genuine happy dance.

I leaned over to my husband and whispered, "That's the best five dollars and sixty-four cents we've ever spent."

And he nodded in agreement.

Smith's delight went on for nearly an hour. He bounced the ball and rolled the ball and hugged the ball. William, Gabriel, and Lorelle all loved their presents too, and I watched them closely and loved the hugs they gave their grandpa and me. And while everyone continued to open and enjoy gifts, Smith just couldn't get over his excitement for that red ball. He held it while he dove into piles of wrapping paper and giggled with perfect happiness. And the entire family couldn't stop laughing over his antics. Each person's pleasure over the gifts they were giving and receiving seemed secondary to observing Smith's exquisite joy.

In the midst of all the delight and chaos, I realized this was a perfect, precious moment, a memory that would never fade. We were all together, we were laughing, we were happy and cozy and filled with the Christmas spirit and the sharing of our family bond.

The next day we were still talking about Smith and agreed that his red ball would go down in our family's history as one of our best Christmas moments.

I'm learning more and more that with Christmas—as with our everyday lives—there are things we can control, and many more things we simply can't. But there are at least as many good things outside of our control as there are bad ones.

We were blessed to have a Christmas free of some of the challenges that had come other years, but I'll never forget how Smith taught me that joy can come so unexpectedly in such simple ways. It's the accumulation of these precious moments scattered intermittently throughout the journey of life that really make all of our efforts—whether great or small—completely worth it. I'm certain that it's more likely than not that I will face next Christmas with new trepidation, and I will have to remind myself of all I've learned in the past in order to have a positive attitude and make the most out of whatever might come. But in spite of the challenges of life, each year has also given me treasured precious moments I can hold in my memory as the reasons why family and love are at the center of all that truly matters at Christmas. And yet I know that even with the absence of what we might consider important or ideal, Christ is always there, He always loves us—each and every one—and it is He who blesses our lives, sometimes in the most unexpected ways.

OTHER BOOKS BY ANITA STANSFIELD

First Love and Forever
First Love, Second Chances
Now and Forever
By Love and Grace
Return to Love
To Love Again
When Forever Comes
A Christmas Melody
For Love Alone
Timeless Waltz
A Time to Dance
Dancing in the Light
A Dance to Remember
The Dickens Inn Series
Volume I, The Best of Times
Volume II, A Far, Far Better Place
Volume III, A Loving Heart
Volume IV, Tranquil Light
Volume V, Every Graceful Fancy
Shadows of Brierley Series
Towers of Brierley
Volume I, The Wanderer
Volume II, A Far Horizon
Volume III, A Distant Shore
Volume IV, In the Valley of the Mountains
Passage on the Titanic
The Wishing Garden
The Garden Path
Legally and Lawfully Yours
Now and Always Yours
The Heir of Brownlie Manor

CHRISTMAS IN JULY

BY BREANNA OLAVESON

The sun had set long ago, but spotlights cut through the darkness as the soundtrack of the pageant boomed over loudspeakers. The atmosphere was alive with joy and whispered anticipation. My costume clung to my back and shoulders as I hiked up the hill through the muggy summer air, fireflies dancing in the trees beyond the path. I cut behind the stage toward the trail leading away from the dressing rooms. It was July in New York, and I was in full costume as a cast member in the Hill Cumorah Pageant. I had a lot of things on my mind, but Christmas certainly wasn't one of them. At least, not yet.

Like most others in the cast, I played more than one part. I had just traded my elaborate dance costume for plain, Native American–style clothes in preparation for my favorite scene: the Savior's visit to the Nephites in America. But I needed to come onto the stage from the far side of the hill, so I walked. I crept around the back of the stage, out of sight of the thousands of people who had come to see the production. The rush of performing in front of such a large crowd combined with the physical exertion of the climb made my heart race.

Then I glanced up at the stage—or what I could see of it from below—and saw something that surprised me. It was a perfect living Nativity: a beautiful young woman with long brown hair knelt on the stage with a baby doll in her arms, a young man standing sentinel behind them both. The spotlight lingered briefly on the family as the narrative described Nephi's vision of the birth of the Savior, then the lights went down. The actors stood, leaving the stage and heading back the way I'd just come.

The encounter gave me pause. In my mind, Mary and Joseph belonged in December, in the cold and the joy of the holiday season. Seeing them portrayed in the heat of the summer felt out of place, like watching football in June or eating pumpkin pie on Memorial Day. But they brought an undeniable spirit of Christmas to this hot summer day I was spending in New York, even if I didn't fully understand why.

The line between reality and imagination blurred often during these performances. I knew the Mary and Joseph I'd seen were part of a dramatization, but the feelings the encounter created in me were genuine.

It had happened before, during rehearsals for the scene I was about to perform in.

Preparing for the scene portraying Christ's visit to America had been a poignant experience. Even though it was sweltering hot at midday and the college student walking across the stage was not actually the Savior, it was easy to get wrapped up in the emotion of the thing. Even now, waiting backstage in costume, I felt joy and anticipation. When I was finally onstage and saw the actor portraying the Savior descend from high above, I didn't have to remind myself to kneel in reverent adoration. In my mind, it felt real.

Do you remember me? I asked in my mind. *Do you remember all the times I've prayed and asked for your peace? Do you remember how I pleaded for help and forgiveness through the Atonement? Do you recognize me?* The moment broke my heart open and incited self-reflection that I had not experienced before. It felt sacred and peaceful.

Sacred, like the nearby grove I'd visited. It was the place where my religion began, and I knew the origin story by heart. But I'd never been to the place where it had all happened—where God the Father and the resurrected Christ appeared to Joseph Smith nearly two centuries ago—and I was happy to be there. Like Christ's appearance in the Americas when He came to the Nephites, He had come to this grove to open the final dispensation and answer young Joseph's important questions. I found a quiet place to sit and read from Joseph Smith's account of the First Vision. The Sacred Grove was appropriately named. I knew the Savior had been there, and the place felt hallowed, serene. This trip to New York, it seemed, had something to teach me about the Savior and His mission.

I saw Mary and Joseph in their place again the next night, a little reminder of where it all began. But even then, I still didn't get it.

* * *

For a while, Mary and Joseph remained part of Christmas celebrations—more important, I knew, than the cookies and the caroling, but essentially in the same category. Every year on Christmas Eve, my family and I ate, sang Christmas carols, acted out the Nativity, read from Luke 2, and went to bed to await the long-anticipated Christmas morning. The story of Christ's birth was an integral part of the celebrations, but it never really touched me again like it had during the Pageant.

Then came Christmas 2013: my first away from the place I'd always called home. More than five years had passed since that summer I spent in New York. I now had a husband, a barely two-year-old daughter, and a brand-new baby. We were young, and because our little family had recently moved twelve hundred miles away from our families, we spent the holiday on our own. It was quiet.

I'd never experienced a Christmas with so little food, so little celebration, and so little noise. When my children went to bed, it was just my husband and me in our little living room. It was cleaner and more comfortable by far than the stable I'd read about every Christmas Eve, but for the first time, I really thought about Mary and Joseph and what that very first Christmas might have been like.

I even had a baby, which seemed appropriate. When I held her that Christmas, I wondered what she would become. I wondered what she would do with her life and what her Heavenly Father had planned for her. I decided it was probably something big. That made me wonder why I was chosen to be her mom and what God needed me to do to raise her. And then I thought about Mary.

That Christmas, she became something more to me than a supporting character in the brief account of the Savior's birth. I saw her as the woman chosen to raise Him, to love Him, to prepare Him for His ministry and His ultimate sacrifice for all mankind. She bore the Savior before He bore us; she carried Him before He carried us; she loved Him as He loves us.

Without Mary and without Joseph, the Savior would not have lived to fulfill His ministry in Jerusalem or to die for the sins of all people. Without the body Mary helped give

Him, He never could have died, He never could have resurrected. He never would have appeared to the Nephites in America or to Joseph Smith in the Sacred Grove or to anyone anywhere else. All of it was possible because of Mary. She was there for the beginning of the Savior's story, and she played an important role in everything that came after.

The Savior said once that He was "Alpha and Omega, the beginning and the end" (3 Nephi 9:18). This moniker is appropriate for the Savior on a number of levels, but in a way, it can also be applied to His mother, who was with Him at the beginning of His life and at the end. All year long, Christians worldwide celebrate the life of Christ. We learn about His ministry, celebrate His triumph over sin and death, and try to emulate His sinless life. But at Christmas, we also remember Mary and her baby boy.

Now when I remember those summer nights I spent in New York so many years ago, I remember the girl who was Mary and the boy who was Joseph. On the quiet Christmases I've spent away from my big family, I've remembered Mary and Joseph, who traveled to a distant country and were alone when "the days were accomplished that she should be delivered" (Luke 2:6). Because of the lessons of that muggy July, every cozy Christmas means something more.

Because Mary was delivered that night, all of us can be delivered too.

OTHER BOOKS BY BREANNA OLAVESON

Mighty Miracles

THE CHRISTMAS CALF

BY ELLEN FAY BELNAP

Once upon an old-time Christmas, way out in the western wilderness, my family lived in an old log house with a dirt roof. One Christmas Eve, when winter winds drifted over barbed wire fences and closed desert roads, an unexpected visitor came to spend Christmas with us in the old log house. When my father pulled him out of drifting snow, Christmas turned wondrous and magical.

It was Christmas Eve, and the old log house was warm and cozy. Mama chucked sagebrush into the cast-iron kitchen stove and slid her spicy pumpkin pies into the oven. My sister Janie was putting the finishing touches on a popcorn chain for the Christmas tree. Lennie sat on the piano stool as I turned the pages of Grandmother's Christmas carols songbook. We had counted the days until Christmas by turning one page a day. "Let's sing 'Silent Night,'" Lennie said. "It's the last song."

Mama looked out the window. "Girls!" she called, "if you want to go check the cattle, you'd better hurry. Your dad's riding down the lane this very minute." Tugging on our coats and boots, my sisters and I ran out to the gate.

Mama called after us, "Forrest, if things get too rough out there, send the girls back."

Daddy waved. "They'll be fine, Elsie." He took rifle shells from the saddle bag and put them in his pocket. "A little excitement never hurt anybody," he mumbled.

Holding the lantern high, Janie rode behind Daddy on his favorite coyote-hunting horse, Old Snakes. Lennie and I brought up the rear, riding on our little pony, Peaches.

As stars popped out of the twilight sky, coyotes on the cliff above the corral yipped and howled. Far across the canyon, their wild brothers answered.

I shivered.

"Do you hear those prairie wolves, girls? They're laughing at us," Daddy said. "Talking dogs—that's what Indians call them—and they're talking, all right, hatching up a hunting party so to kill every calf from here to the Snake River. Wouldn't be a bit surprised if some of those devils have calf hide stuck between their teeth come morning. Keep your eyes peeled for tracks, girls."

In the field, the ghostly white faces of the cattle shone in the moonlight. Steamy breath rose from their nostrils. The wild cry of the coyotes echoed through the black canyon walls. "Look out there in the sagebrush, girls," Daddy whispered. "There in the shadows. See those eyes gleaming like the devil himself. It's a coyote, sure as death. Get your holts, girls." Daddy raised his rifle. I grabbed the saddle horn. Lennie hugged me tightly. Two shots rang out and then a yelp. Little Peaches stepped sideways. Old Snakes snorted and stomped. "Easy now," Daddy said. "Easy."

The horses settled down, but my heart pounded wildly.

A low mournful bellow rang through the frosty air. Daddy held the lantern high, casting the dim light over a small red heifer and her newly born calf.

"Easy now, girl," Daddy said. "You're going to be all right, but it looks like your calf is in trouble." Swinging off Old Snakes, he bent over the little calf, brushed ice and snow from its hide, and rubbed it down with a gunnysack. "Poor little critter," he said, "half frozen this way. It'll be a mighty miracle if you live through the night." He wrapped the calf in a gunnysack, gently lifted it onto his saddle, and said, "Keep breathing, little fella. We're going to take you home."

He walked back to the exhausted little heifer and patted her on the neck. She struggled to raise her hind legs, fell back with a whooshing thud, and let out a long, high cry. "She's mighty weak," Daddy called, "but we can't leave her here, or she'll be a goner for sure."

The heifer lunged forward and fell back again. Finally Daddy took hold of her tail. "Sorry to have to do this," he said. He gave her tail a hard twist, and the poor thing lunged to her feet and stood there trembling in the moonlight.

A sob caught in my throat. I wiped away hot tears.

"Good girl!" Janie called. "Good girl!"

Swinging into the saddle, Daddy scooted the calf up close to the horn and started for home. Trailing along behind Old Snakes, the heifer bawled frantically after her calf, her cries echoing in the cliffs. High on the rim rock the coyotes answered. A chilling wind cut through my clothes and set my teeth to chattering. Slowly we moved on until, finally, the faint light of Mama's lamp flickered through the darkness.

"Faydee," Daddy called. "Whip Peaches over and under, and go tell your mom I'm coming with the calf."

Happy to be heading home, Peaches trotted right along.

"Mama, Mama!" Lennie and I cried as we burst through the kitchen door. "Daddy found a newborn calf in the snow, and he's half frozen!"

"Run and get some gunnysacks," Mama ordered. Quickly she made a gunnysack bed in a round tin tub and set it close to the stove.

When we heard heavy boots on the porch, Lennie ran to open the door.

Daddy placed the little calf in his new, snug bed.

"Look, he can't even hold up his head," Lennie said.

"Is he dead?" I asked.

"Not yet," Daddy said.

Out by the porch, the little heifer bawled and bellowed, still crying for her calf.

A lump caught in my throat. "How can we help her, Daddy?" I asked.

"We've already helped her," Daddy said. "It only takes a couple of coyotes to kill a cow and her calf. We were lucky this time. Don't worry about her crying for her calf. That's a good sign."

Mama chucked sprigs of sagebrush and cedar boughs into the fire. They sputtered and popped, and soon the old log house was filled with their spicy fragrance.

"What shall we name him?" Janie whispered.

Daddy took off his gloves and warmed his hands by the fire. "He can't have a name. He's a wild thing and has to stay with his mother."

Lennie knelt by the tub. "Can't he have a name just for tonight, Daddy?"

"How about the Christmas Calf?" Mama said.

"It's a magical name," I whispered. "A perfectly perfect magical name."

With the Christmas Calf now dry and warm, Daddy lit the lantern and left to drive the cow to the barn. Her terrible bellowing faded into the night.

I sat by the wood box watching the Christmas Calf breathe in and out, in and out. "Wake up," I whispered.

But he didn't blink an eye.

"Why don't you sing him a song?" Mama said.

And so we sang the little calf every Christmas carol we'd ever heard. I held my baby brother, Stephen, up to see, but the calf didn't stir. The fire burned low. My sisters and I went out to bring in wood. As we filled our arms with sagebrush and cedar, we saw the lantern light.

"Look up at the Milky Way, girls," Daddy shouted from behind the lantern's glow. "We've got Christmas lights. More stars than we can possibly count! More blessings than we can possibly contain!"

Looking up, we whirled around and around, shouting, "Christmas lights! Christmas lights!" The stars all whirled together like sky fire.

We filled the wood box, and I told the Christmas Calf all about the Christmas stars. How on the first Christmas night the stars were blazing away, but one star shone brighter than all the rest. When the Wise Men saw the star, they jumped for joy and followed its light through the desert until they found baby Jesus.

Sitting with his feet propped on the oven door, Daddy read the story of Christmas by the flaring coal-oil lamp. His voice rose and fell in a musical cadence. Janie knelt by the little calf's tub and held Stephen up to see. Lennie scooted closer.

"Look! He's opening his eyes," she whispered.

Carefully, I took Grandmother's Christmas carol songbook off the piano. Kneeling by the Christmas Calf, I showed him all the pictures of the very first Christmas.

"This is baby Jesus in the manger and Mary and Joseph," I whispered. "See the donkey? And there you are, lying in the hay, watching the shepherds and Wise Men kneeling by the manger. And see? There's baby Jesus. Do you know Jesus?"

"All creatures know Jesus," Janie said.

I turned the page, and Janie whispered, "There I am singing, 'Oh, Come, All Ye Faithful,' with all those people by the cathedral. I'm the girl in the beautiful bonnet and the velvet dress that reaches down to my button-up shoes. And look, Lennie, there you are with your hands in a fancy fur muff, and—"

"Girls, are you listening?" Daddy said. "What did I just read?"

Quick as anything, Janie spoke up. "You were at the part where King Herod lied to the Wise Men and tried to trick them into coming back to tell him where they found Jesus."

"Very good!" Daddy said and went on reading.

I turned another songbook page. What I saw took my breath away. I must have looked at this picture a hundred times and never noticed, but there I was, a little shepherd girl sitting on a hill overlooking the town of Bethlehem. I looked closer. That was me, all right. I was holding a shepherds' crook, and there was my sheep dog. We were gazing up at the Star of Bethlehem. I couldn't believe it! I was in the Christmas story! I blinked back tears.

Daddy had finished reading and was stoking the fire. "We'd best let the calf get some sleep. He'll have a big day tomorrow when we take him back to his mother in the barn."

After we ate a supper of spicy stew and mincemeat pie, Mama stuffed the Christmas goose and put it in the oven. We all found Santa socks. Daddy let me have a big wool work sock with a hole in the heel. I fixed it with a safety pin.

Janie put homemade taffy on a plate for Santa and wrote a note.

Dear Santa,

Please put a lump of coal in the stove so the little Christmas Calf will stay warm.

P. S. We've been mostly good. Love, Janie, Ellen Fay (Faydee for short), Lennie Lou and little Stephen.

Mama blew out the lamp and opened the stove door. Firelight danced on the Christmas tree ornaments and flickered in the silvery tinsel. In dark corners, the shadows swayed. A hush filled the room. "Maybe the calf will fall asleep now," Mama whispered.

We sang all the quiet carols. The music swirled around us, and a beautiful warm feeling crept over me.

Was this the Christmas Spirit? I wondered.

"Silent night! Holy night! All is calm, all is bright. . ." Mama filled the hot-water bottle with steaming water from the kettle, then we tiptoed off to our frosty bed and slid the bottle between the sheets. Snuggled there with my sisters, I soon fell asleep.

I woke in the dark to the sound of a strange tapping. I held my breath and listened. There it was again. Tap. . . tap. . . tap!

"Janie," I whispered. "Wake up! Listen!"

Rat-a-tat, rat-a tat! Rat-a-tat-tat.

"Janie, wake up! Hear that?"

"I don't hear anything," she mumbled.

Tap. . . tap. . . tap—Rat-a-tat, rat-a-tat, rat-a-tat-tat-tat!

I shook Lennie. "There it goes again."

Rat-a-tat-tat-tat-tat!

Janie sat up.

"What is it?" Lennie said sleepily.

Janie threw back the covers. “It’s Santa’s reindeer on the roof,” she whispered. “Listen!”

Rat-a-tat, rat-a-tat-tat-tat.

“Come on!” I said.

Shivering, we crept out of bed and shuffled along in the dim light to the kitchen door. The sound of reindeer hooves grew louder. Janie opened the door a crack.

“It’s too dark,” Lennie said, taking one step into the kitchen.

Tap, tap, tap. Rat-a-tat-tat-tat-tat!

At that very moment, a little reindeer brushed past us in the dark. We jumped back.

“It’s Dasher!” I shouted.

Our parents’ bedroom door burst open, and a dim lamplight cast shadows all around. “Ho, ho, ho! Merry Christmas!” Daddy called.

Mama appeared in the doorway, holding the baby.

Then quick as a wink, out of the shadows jumped the little Christmas Calf.

“It’s the Christmas Calf!” we shouted. “Look, Stephen! It’s the Christmas Calf!” We jumped, shouted, and clapped. Stephen clapped too.

Rat-a-tat-tat. The little Christmas Calf pranced past us.

“‘Now, Dasher! Now, Dancer! Now, Prancer and Vixen! On, Comet! On, Cupid! On, Donner and Blitzen!’” we all said together. Around and around the table we galloped, our shadows dancing on the white-washed walls, the Christmas Calf leading us on a merry chase. “‘To the top of the porch, to the top of the wall, now dash away, dash away, dash away all!’”

Daddy’s voice rose above the din. “Hold on, girls. Don’t get him too excited. Look at the little fella. He’s plum out of breath." Daddy set the lamp on the sideboard. "Well, I'll be jiggered! Look here! The Christmas Calf has left us a fresh Christmas pie on the floor by the Christmas tree."

We laughed and clapped and shouted. "A Christmas pie! A Christmas pie! All on a Christmas morning!"

Pretty as you please, the little calf trotted over to Mama's chair and looked at Stephen curiously.

"He's had enough excitement," Daddy said. "I'll bring Old Snakes round and take him to the barn. His mother might not take him back if we wait too long. You keep him calmed down till I get back." He put on his sheepskin coat, lit the lantern, and left for the barn.

"Let's scoop up that little calf pie," Mama said as she seated herself in Grandfather's old Morgan chair. Stephen held out his little arms. The Christmas Calf walked over to him and stood there blinking.

"Did you see Santa, little calf?" Mama asked. "I bet he tickled you behind your ears."

The calf took a step forward.

Lennie gasped. "You mean the Christmas Calf saw Santa?"

Mama nodded. "Sure, he did."

"He saw the real Santa, not the fake cardboard one in the grocery store window with the soda pop in his hand?"

Mama smiled. "No, not the fake one."

"Oh, I wish I could have seen the look on Santa's face when he read my note and found the Christmas Calf," Janie said. "I bet he never saw a Christmas Calf before."

"Probably not," Mama agreed.

The Christmas Calf had already seen the big spinning top and the bubbling bird whistles Santa had left under our tree. But when we blew our bird whistles and showed him our oranges, he acted surprised.

A pale dawn was breaking over the eastern cliffs. My sisters and I followed Old Snakes and the Christmas Calf to the barn, with the icy air stinging our cheeks.

"Best you don't come into the barn, girls," Daddy said. He scooped the calf up in his arms, and Janie opened the door a crack. From inside the barn came a long, mournful bellow.

My sisters and I climbed up the frozen manure pile and leaned in the window. The barn was dank and dark. A shaft of lantern light shone through the doorway. The heifer's ghostly white face, with its bulging eyes, popped out of the darkness. I gasped and clamped a hand over my mouth.

"Shh! Quiet," Janie whispered.

The white face opened its huge mouth, stretched out its long red neck, and let out another mournful cry. The barn door opened wide, and holding the lantern high, Daddy urged the Christmas Calf forward. The heifer let out a soft moo and trotted over to the Christmas Calf. Lovingly she licked his face, and then he nudged her in the belly, searching under her flank. His little tail wagged happily.

"He's found his breakfast," Lennie whispered.

Joyfully, we trooped home to tell Mama the good news.

In the evening, when the Big Dipper hung over the western cliff and the Christmas stars lit up one by one, I tramped through the deep snow to visit the Christmas Calf. My uncle's hired man, Chuck, who had been helping Daddy chop through the ice on top of the hay stack, was there pitching down hay to the little heifer. Leaning through the barn window, I told him all about how I loved Christmas Eve. How we sang Christmas carols to the Christmas Calf, and how he loved the Christmas carol songbook. Chuck didn't say a word. So I told about the Christmas Calf prancing around the kitchen table just like Dasher and Dancer and Prancer and Vixen, how he saw Santa, and how he loved hearing us blow our bird whistles. Still, Chuck didn't say anything. I took a deep breath. I had saved the best for last. "The little Christmas Calf is magic," I said triumphantly.

Chuck stopped pitching hay. "Well, he might have seen Santa," he said, "but that doesn't mean he's magic."

"Oh, yes, sir! He is too magic!" I said firmly. "He made Christmas magical!"

Chuck was quiet, like he was thinking the magic part over real hard. I waited. Finally he nodded. "Whatever you say." He smiled. "Whatever you say."

I wanted to tell Chuck the rest, but I figured if he couldn't catch on to the magical part of Christmas right off, he'd never catch on to the wondrous part. So I told everything to the Christmas Calf. How I loved showing him the songbook, finding myself in the Christmas story, singing all the Christmas carols—all the wonders of Christmas Eve.

Walking home through lightly falling snow, I thought of the little Christmas songbook. I wanted to search for more Christmas secrets in its pages before Mama tucked it away in her keepsake chest. I found her sitting in Grandfather's old Morgan chair, darning the hole in the Santa sock I'd fixed with a safety pin.

I took down Grandmother's songbook and lovingly turned the pages.

"Find something interesting?" Mama asked.

"There's a picture of me here on page thirty-six," I said. "See? I'm this little shepherd girl right here in the Christmas story."

Mama put away her mending and lit the lamp. "Yes, that is you," she said, smiling down at me. "Just remember, we're all in the Christmas story."

"Really? You mean every single person in the whole world?"

"Yes, every single person in the whole wide world. We're all in the story of Christmas."

Mama and I were quiet for a long time. I finally got up the courage to ask the question I'd been thinking of since Christmas Eve. "Will we ever have another Christmas like this one?"

"Of course we will, Faydee."

"I mean a magical, wondrous Christmas."

Mama held me close. "The magic of Christmas is fun," she said. "It comes and goes, but the wonder of Christmas goes on forever."

"So it can never ever be lost!"

"No, never."

"Can we keep the Christmas songbook on the piano for a while?" I asked.

Mama smiled. "I think that would be a good idea."

Daddy came in with a bucket of fresh foaming milk. "You girls can't keep going up to the barn so often," he said. "The little heifer doesn't take kindly to visitors. The calf will be strong enough to be turned out into the field with his mother in a day or two. It's time to let the little Christmas Calf go with the wild bunch."

The winter moon rose over the canyon. My sisters and I took our little brother out to see the Christmas stars. Our steamy breath billowed out into the icy air. "Merry Christmas," we shouted. "Merry Christmas to the little Christmas Calf. Merry Christmas to the whole wide world!"

Up on the rim rock, the coyotes howled.

BETTER TO RECEIVE THAN TO GIVE

BY GANEL-LYN CONDIE

I paid the dental bill and had enough money for four new car tires. All the bills were now—*finally*—caught up.

I let out a deep, cleansing sigh of relief and felt the tension in my shoulders suddenly relax.

Almost three years earlier, my husband had lost his job. It was the first time in over twenty-three years of marriage that we had experienced the great refining reality of unemployment. Losing over $80,000 on our home, surviving on savings and food storage, and selling most of our earthly possessions, we moved into a small rental home, and our family started back down the road of financial recovery. That long period took a toll on us but also breathed new life into our family connections. We learned lessons of faith and trust, and constant reminders of what really mattered seemed to trickle in and change us for the better.

Now Rob was again working, this time as a CFO at a steel company. Our family resettled in a new county, with very little, and joyfully started into a simpler lifestyle. With help from a special program, we eventually moved out of our tiny rental farmhouse into a new home of our own, and deals on *KSL Classifieds* helped replace furnishings we had previously sold.

But on this particular day, many months after the initial layoff, after the move, after the resettlement, and after the bills being paid, it suddenly felt different, like we were going to make it! Hope came flooding into my mind as I wrote the check out for the dentist.

Then the phone rang.

It was three o'clock in the afternoon. Rob was calling to say he was on his way home.

Anxiously, I asked, "Why? It's too early."

"I was just laid off," he whispered, then fell silent for a moment. "I don't have a job."

There was a rushing in my ears, like all the air was being sucked out of me. Moments earlier I'd been breathing, but now that all-too-familiar gripping feeling in my chest, the one that had finally relaxed just moments before, was back.

Saving money again wasn't an option. Building up our food storage again was not going to happen. There would be no lawn or landscaping for our empty dirt lot. Forget planning a family vacation. Back again was that oh-so-familiar survival feeling of thick fog.

* * *

The tears on Rob's face matched the ones stuck inside my throat. It felt different this time. As he walked in from the garage, we held each other and cried. He asked why. I asked why. As Rob explained in more detail what had happened, I could see this time was going to be different. This time, the first layoff felt like a faith-promoting experience, a trial that would teach us. An experience with unemployment wasn't that uncommon. But two rounds of it? What was this second time supposed to do for us?

We called a friend, who came right away to give us both priesthood blessings. The words from Rob's blessing seared into my mind: "All of your needs are known by God. And He will make sure all of your family's needs will be met during this time. Receive the service that will be given you." The powerful impression we all had after the blessings was that this period of unemployment would not go on for a lengthy period of time. It was early July . . . and we had to trust in God's timetable.

Rob being home more was a good thing. We found a new routine. But with no financial reserve, garden veggies to harvest, or a severance package to rely on, things felt uncertain. But the blessing, the promise from God, was that *our needs were known and would be met.* We filed for unemployment, and Rob quickly set up a temporary home office upstairs in the guest/craft room, where he could get to busy finding a job. He started networking. I helped by sharing on social media. And the job leads started coming in. Interviews happened regularly enough to keep our hopes up, but there was nothing of real promise on the job horizon.

The summer progressed with no real prospects of employment. Each day and week that passed saw our gratitude list grow and our bank account shrink. I started sharing "Miracles in the Mess" posts on social media as a way to focus on daily blessings, what was working instead of what wasn't, while Rob was unemployed.

God helped us through the unknown with helpers. People would anonymously squeeze money through the front door. I remember the day we needed to put gas in both of our cars. After paying the bills, there wasn't anything left for the week. I stopped at the mailbox, and instead of more bills,

I found a card. It was from a college friend I hadn't had contact with for over twenty-four years. She wrote me a beautiful note thanking me for my example of faith both in the past and during our current situation. Included in the letter was a gift card that was just the right amount to fill up our gas tanks.

As the summer came to a close, concerns about how to buy school supplies and clothing for my kids weighed heavily on my mind. Hopes for a quick unemployment season seemed to be moving into a "longer than we thought" phase. Each time we would panic or worry about how to make it all work, I would recall the words of that blessing on the first day. *Our needs were known and would be met!* One day a friend texted me to say she had left a gift on our back porch and wanted to make sure I got it. This dear mother was also trying to buy school supplies and clothes for her own four children, so when I opened the gift she had left me, I gasped. It was a gift card for more than enough to buy my kids all they would need to start school.

Gratitude and love were the first feelings that flooded my heart. But with all the service we received, families were giving to us what they needed for themselves. I didn't need to see bank statements to know that angels were sacrificing to bless our family. Our back-porch gift brought guilt to my heart. How could we keep accepting help from so many neighbors and family members? These good Samaritans were definitely not the Rockefellers. So many were just middle-class families trying to pay for braces and electricity, but they were still reaching out to serve us.

But I also realized I had to remember, our needs were known and would be met. And we must *receive*.

* * *

I kept thinking, praying, and hoping that we would surely be employed by Halloween, and if not then, by Christmas! Right?

Orange pumpkin candies and jack-o'-lanterns filled the grocery-store shelves. The leaves were changing, but our job situation wasn't. But the promises God had made us continued to manifest themselves almost daily. Help from neighbors and extended family kept us swimming.

One night, a dear couple handed me a check, first making me promise I would take it before I saw the amount. The total of their generous gift was the exact amount we were short in paying the mortgage for the month. Sometimes the needs were small, less than a house payment, but no matter the size of the need or the value of the gift, everything given came from God.

Rob humbly went every two weeks to the bishop's storehouse to fill food orders for our family. Miraculously, our pantry started to fill with food. On one particular visit to the storehouse, Rob was accompanied by a special missionary helper. This sister missionary walked with him up and down the Church's grocery aisle, just like every other visit. But she was different from the others because she wasn't a stranger. She was Rob's previous boss's mother! My husband's humility was inspiring. He smiled and thanked her. Could I have done that? He not only had the grace to receive help from the Church—but also to receive service from his ex-boss's own mother.

Thanksgiving was now right around the corner. That tightening in my chest seemed to be growing with each passing week. I prayed while paying bills. And cried each time another anonymous donor would knock on our door and run. The needs of our family were being met just as our Father had promised. But the receiving part of service was starting to feel like shoes that were just a little too tight. At first they felt a little uncomfortable, but as time wore on, the constriction grew more intense. I knew God had asked us to *receive* service, but some days, I didn't want to *receive* any more; I wanted to be the giver.

People started sending me messages about how our unemployment was inspiring them. My social media posts were inviting others to focus more on gratitude. Families that were also unemployed or underemployed started to share instead of keeping it hidden. In their honesty, neighbors and friends started to reach out and serve one another more often. Even in the discomfort, I could see the good coming from the bad.

* * *

Christmas was coming. But, still, the job wasn't. What would we do? How could we do another holiday without employment? Our family had always been the sub-for-Santa gifters and had served at the shelter or organized winter-coat drives. We did diaper drives and donated Halloween candy to the homeless. Now we couldn't give to others in the same way we had in the past. This year we could give only prayers and thanksgiving, not the usual trinkets and treasures. This year was about learning to really, deeply receive.

As the decorations went up, we reminisced about the passing year. But the constant nagging in our minds never ever disappeared completely. The unemployment benefit deadline was quickly approaching. The money wasn't a lot—it barely covered our mortgage—but it helped. If Rob didn't find a new job by the new year, we would be in major financial crisis.

As December passed, we enjoyed our family time together. My kids were amazing! They never complained. When people asked them what they wanted for Christmas, Cameron and Brooklyn would always say, "We are great. We don't need anything." Those were my moments of motherly pride as I saw into my children's good hearts. Condie Christmases never had been about piles of gifts, even back when we had abundance, but a mom wants to give her kids a *little* something. So we waited upon the Lord, and the miracles continued.

* * *

One day, I got a call from friends from the old neighborhood. They had lived by us during our first job loss. You know, back when we had some resources to pull from. The Guys (that's what we always call them) said they wanted to visit on Saturday. I didn't think much about it since it had been a few months since our regular get-together. Saturday morning came with a knock at the door, and The Guys came inside to chat. We caught up on their lives and ours. Then they slyly said, "We have some things for you in the car."

Within minutes, our Christmas season of receiving started to multiply. They carried in boxes of food and gifts, including things not available at the storehouse. It was as if God had texted them a list of all those little items we hadn't purchased for so long. And then after the last box was unloaded, our dear friends stopped and handed us an envelope. They reported that our friends in the old neighborhood had collected all of the food and gifts. And as I opened the envelope and pulled out a pile of cash, the bills we needed to pay didn't look impossible anymore. I cried and smiled and cried some more.

I am sure our friends thought I was crying because of the generosity of their gifts. The money they gave would save us, and their generosity was overwhelming, but it was about so much more than that.

Since our July layoff, the blessings from many beloved people had never stopped. But that Saturday morning, I cried and hugged those Christmas elves tighter, not because of what they had brought in boxes but because of what they had given my heart. I hadn't thought our old neighbors really missed us that much. After five years of living among them, serving and connecting, I often questioned if real bonds had ever been forged. So when The Guys carried those boxes into our kitchen and handed me the envelope of donations from those very friends I had questioned, I was proven wrong. We did matter. The bonds were still in place.

That Christmas delivery had been much more than money and supplies. I received something only God knew I needed, something not found in stores. As I whispered a few more tearful thank-yous to my dear old friends, the message God had been trying to teach me since July was suddenly crystal clear: it is sometimes better to receive than to give.

* * *

That holiday was truly unforgettable. I will always remember how my children didn't ask for anything—but *received* much. Christmas morning came and went, and we were still unemployed. That December wasn't about the worry and stress of unemployment though. No, that Christmas was a testimony of God keeping His promises. When He says our needs are known and will be met, they always are and always will be. Not every prayer is answered in the way we ask, but I know that all prayers are answered.

The unemployment went much longer than we'd expected or was comfortable, but looking back, it went on long enough for us to learn what was needful. God was trying to teach us greater faith and to trust in Him.

After the new year, Rob took a new job.

The following Christmas was very different. We had the money to put up Christmas lights, pay bills, and give gifts to others.

But I had already learned that Christmas is so much more than giving.

The ultimate gift given was a baby born in Bethlehem and placed in a manger. The Savior of the world came for me. And He came for the entire universe. Jesus did what no one else could do. And nothing I could ever give would match God's grace.

He only asks that I truly *receive*.

OTHER BOOKS BY GANEL-LYN CONDIE

I Can Do Hard Things with God
I Can Forigve with God

THE CHRISTMAS TRAIN

BY JENNIFER MOORE

Ever since I could remember, one of my family's Christmas traditions was going to see Marmé and Par's train. Marmé and Par are my grandparents, and seeing the train wasn't an event; it was an experience. We showed up any evening after Thanksgiving, and Marmé and Par welcomed us with hugs and hung up our coats. We all trooped downstairs to the family room, where Par had a warm fire crackling in the fireplace. Marmé brought a tray with treats—usually the chocolate kind—and cocoa, or Coke on ice for the adults, all arranged prettily with Christmas napkins. Marmé was all about the details.

The train wasn't just a train. They moved the furniture to create space because the display occupied an entire side of the room. Luminescent flecks sprinkled over a bed of cotton twinkled in the light. Small painted houses with warm inner glows dotted the landscape amid a forest of pine trees. There was an ice-skating pond made from a mirror, pathways of teeny cobblestones, and little ceramic figures in Victorian-era dress who happily caroled, visited, sledded down a snowy hill, or called out from their carts.

Surrounding the Dickens-eque winter wonderland, the train moved at a steady clip along its winding track, through a tunnel, and over a bridge.

The entire thing took Par days to set up. Risers and extension cords were hidden beneath artificial snow, then snaked carefully under the track, and by the time we arrived, all we saw was an idyllic old-fashioned holiday scene.

We chatted with Marmé and Par and usually a few other family members who had stopped by at the same time, or sometimes we sat quietly, watching by firelight, our gazes moving with the train around the track. The kids loved to find the hidden Grinch figurine that Uncle Jim managed to conceal every year. They called it a cameo.

It was always nostalgic and pleasant, and my memories of those times are warm. I'd never given much thought to the tradition or why we did it. Until it stopped.

A few years ago, everything changed. Marmé and Par moved into a condo, and because of health problems and a lack of space, they didn't set up the train.

While I visited with Marmé this year after her hip surgery, I told her I missed the train and asked about it. How had the tradition started? Why a train?

Her answer was unexpected and made me think of the word *tradition* in a different light. I'll try to tell it in her words as well as I remember them.

"I suppose trains remind me of my father, Grover." She patted her red wavy curls. Marmé is one who manages to look put together in a hospital gown and oxygen tube.

"Grover loved my mother, Alice, from the moment they met in Mexico—you see, mother grew up in the Mormon colonies, and Grover moved there from Illinois because of health problems. That's how they treated asthma back then—sent you somewhere hot and dry. But my grandmother,

Anna Margretha, was a strict Danish woman. She didn't think Grover was good enough for her daughter and took Alice away to Salt Lake. Father followed and finally convinced Mother to marry him. He was just crazy about her."

She smiled, no doubt thinking of her parents young and in love. "You have to understand, Jenny, things were different then." Marmé settled back into her chair, wincing at the ache from her broken hip. "During the Depression, many men had to leave their families to find work. My father lost his job, and although he tried to find work in Salt Lake, there was nothing. My mother suffered a stroke when I was born that left half of her body paralyzed. She had been a secretary for the mayor, a really important woman and well respected, but after her stroke, it was hard enough for her to take care of the home and her children. She couldn't work too."

As she spoke, I tried to remember stories I'd heard about my great-grandmother Alice. I knew she'd been partially paralyzed and could hardly speak, but I had always thought of her as an old woman, not a young mother. Her disability must have been devastating to her family.

Marmé must have been thinking the same thing. She swallowed and cleared her throat before continuing. "Father did all he could to keep food on the table. I remember him riding home on his bicycle with a tomato plant for us to put in our garden. Heaven knows where he found it. Finally he got work with the Union Pacific Railroad. Sometimes he was a conductor, wearing a vest and taking tickets, and sometimes he worked as a rail man, with striped overalls and a soft-brimmed hat—just like you see in the movies." She smiled, giving me a moment to think of exactly how an old-fashioned train man looked. I thought of characters from *Dumbo* and *The Polar Express*.

"We were the poorest family in our neighborhood, but because Father could get passes for the train, that was one thing special about us that none of the other kids had.

Back then, taking a trip on the train was a big deal. An event. It meant wearing your nicest clothes. We would curl our hair and put on our best dresses, gloves, and hats when we went to visit Father. The trips were difficult for Mother. She packed us a lunch in a shoebox since we couldn't afford to buy food on the train, and then we helped her climb aboard, and she limped with her dragging leg to a seat beside the window.

"One time, we took the train down to where Father worked at a station in Nevada. They needed to take the engine up the line a few miles, and Father let me ride on the very front, behind the cow-catcher. Just me and him. He held on to me the whole time, even though I was old enough not to fall. When we returned to the station, he cooked dinner for us in the red caboose.

"Whenever I heard a train whistle, I thought of Father, far away, taking tickets or moving luggage at the station. And as he was away for longer periods of time, my memories of him started to combine with the trains."

I nodded, imagining my grandmother as a young girl in her best dress, hat, and gloves standing with her father on the front of a black engine with coal and soot everywhere. The memory was nearly eighty years old but still made her smile.

"One year, right before Christmas, we got word that my old Danish grandmother, Anna Margretha, had died. She lived in Idaho Falls with her sister by this time. We hadn't seen Father for quite a while, but somehow he heard the news and sent passes for us to take the train to Idaho for the funeral. Grover and his mother-in-law, Anna

Margretha, never had a close relationship, but he still gave up the passes for us to go."

I wondered if he received only a certain number of passes per year and if sacrificing these meant he couldn't travel home himself, but when I asked Marmé, she wasn't sure exactly how it worked. She'd been too young to pay attention to those sorts of details.

"Aunt Lily met us at the station with a long dark automobile. It was quite the thing to ride in an automobile then; we'd hardly ever had a chance. Aunt Lily was a nervous person and a terrible driver. She took a turn too quick, and we ended up in a ditch on a country road. We had to wait for a team to pull the car out. It's hard to imagine now, but they hitched horses to the front of the car and dragged it out of the ditch." Marmé laughed at the memory, and I was glad an automobile accident on her way to a funeral wasn't a terrible memory.

"So you remember that Christmas and your dad giving you tickets to go to your grandma's funeral, and that's why trains are so special to you?" I ventured.

She shrugged. "Partly, I guess. While Par was in the service, we lived all over the US and Europe. Trains were just how people got around then. A train whistle meant we were going somewhere or someone was coming to visit. Lots of times it meant Par was home. And sometimes it meant he was leaving. But it always meant something."

She was quiet for a moment. "The whistles are much different in Europe, you know."

"I didn't know."

"More of a screech. Terrible sound." Marmé shook her head. "American engines make a pleasant whistle. Sort of a *poof*." She lifted her hands outward to illustrate. "Like in old Westerns."

"Trains were memories," she said. "Not just of my father or of Christmas but of how life was. I guess they mean different things to different people."

I thought about what she said. While it would have been nice to have a tidy metaphor for the trains, this was realistic. Memories change, feelings change, and while the Christmas train reminds Marmé of riding on the front of the engine with her father behind the cow-catcher, it reminds Par of returning home to his family after a long assignment or shipping off to combat.

To me, it means happy evenings sitting by the fire in my grandparents' family room, chatting with cousins, with the steady hum of the model train in the background and a cup of cocoa in my hands.

After the visit, Marmé's story was on my mind a lot. It's nice to have something definite to assign to a tradition. "We do this because . . ." or "This reminds us of . . ." or even "Every year, we do it exactly like this . . ." But the truth is, like Marmé said, memories mean different things to different people. Traditions change and evolve. They sometimes go away altogether, and sometimes new ones are created. Sort of like trains, I thought, feeling philosophical. Sometimes they get worn out or replaced or updated.

The glimpse into Marmé's past made me sad for a tradition that was over. Knowing the reasons behind it and the closeness she felt to her traveling father, I felt a sense of loss for the Christmas train and what it represented.

Until the day after Thanksgiving when I received a phone call from my dad.

He wondered if my kids would come out to his house with their cousins to help set up a train and watch *The Polar Express*. And when I hung up the phone, I realized the tradition of the Christmas train had chugged on down the track into the next generation.

OTHER BOOKS BY JENNIFER MOORE

Becoming Lady Lockwood

Lady Emma's Campaign

Miss Burton Unmasks a Prince

Simply Anna

Lady Helen Finds Her Song

THE LONG WAY HOME

KRISTA LYNNE JENSEN

In December of 1989, I was young, idealistic, broke, and stranded. BYU campus would hold me prisoner for Christmas if I didn't find a way from Provo, Utah, to Kennewick, Washington, soon. As pretty as campus was in the snow, with the mountains tall and bright under blue skies, I didn't want to be there for the holidays. I really didn't want to be there.

My sophomore year of college was actually my first year away from home. I'd transferred to BYU after a year of community college and was pursuing an art degree. I was the oldest of four kids, the first to leave the nest, the first to share an apartment with five roommates, and the first to suffer from an acute bout of homesickness. The homesickness surprised me. I'd always been independent. My "I can do it by myself" attitude had been part of the package deal since the minute I was born. The story is that I chose not to cry, and when the doctor swatted my bottom so I would subsequently clear my lungs, I simply lifted my head and glared at him. *Then* I cried.

From that day forward, my independent nature became legendary—at least it did in my tight little family unit. To the rest of the world, I was painfully shy and polite and just tried to keep my head above water on a campus with a roiling current.

I was born a paradox: very brave and very afraid. And that year, I was afraid of not making it home for Christmas.

I shouldn't have been. In the end, my parents figured it out. They're resourceful that way. How could they not be? My mom is a creative genius, and my dad is a brilliant engineer. Being adorable people didn't hurt either. They conked their adorable heads together and found the solution. Where was the answer? Right under my nose. Or down the hall and to the left.

My cousin Cassi Bates shared my apartment. She and her brother Sean were signed up to take a charter bus hired by Spokane, Washington, parents to get their BYU students safely home for the holidays. As luck would have it, my parents were able to get me the last seat on that bus. So I joyously packed and looked forward to that sixteen-hour bus ride to Spokane, which was almost home. Nearly. Once there, my grandparents—also Spokane-ites—would pick me up from the bus and drive the remaining two and a half hours to Kennewick, and I would be home.

Home! I was exultant. It was a longer route than the usual eleven-hour jaunt from Provo through Boise to Kennewick, taking us instead through Wyoming, across Montana, through northern Idaho, and then to Spokane, but I was grateful! Our bus left at midnight, so we would be sleeping for most of the trip. Sleep! That state of being that increases in value the older you get, the more finals you study for, the more heavy books you have to read to pass a class. We would sleep. I was delirious with gratitude.

At midnight on the evening of our departure, an assembly of groggy students met on campus, had prayer, and boarded the charter bus. I quickly observed, in the way that sophomores do, that most of the kids were freshmen from the dorms. We found seats and arranged ourselves with pillows, stuffed animals, headphones, and books in half-lidded, half-awake stupors. I got as comfortable as I could, put my seat back, and closed my eyes as the bus lurched forward. Ah, the beginning of our journey, and I would dream through most of it.

Wrong.

Those half-awake stupors quickly morphed into fully awake adolescence crammed into a dorm-on-wheels. It became clear that the girl I sat next to had no intention of sleeping because she was more interested in the two boys sitting in front of us. The majority of the students seemed to have the same idea. There would be no sleeping. No. Sleep.

My gratitude dissipated like breath-fog on glass.

To be honest, I might have been more enthusiastic about the boys if they'd been *mature*, but, as I mentioned, they were mere freshmen, and I was more interested in the backs of my eyelids. I dug into my backpack and pulled out a book, trying to ignore the boy leaning over the back of my chair, throwing something to a seat up and across the aisle. My seatmate stood as well. She giggled and shouted a conversation with some friends in the back.

You know that toddler toy you push around? It's a little clear dome on wheels with a long handle, and as you push it through the house, little colorful balls pop around—pop, pop, pop. *Pop*. That was our bus. All through Wyoming and most of Montana. *Pop*, *pop*, pop, *POP*. At midnight. Pop, *pop*, pop, *pop*. In the snow steadily falling. *POP, POP, POP*. It must have looked quite festive from the outside.

We stopped somewhere blanketed in white to put on snow chains. I watched the snow with bleary eyes and jealousy. It must've been blissfully quiet out there in the still hours of morning. I looked at my cousins, who'd chosen the very back seat. Wise. Sean snuggled into his far corner under a blanket, his sleeping face haloed in slumber, his mouth smushed slightly open against his pillow. Cassi wore headphones, completely absorbed in a book. She must have felt my gaze because she looked up.

"Want to trade?" I mouthed, waggling my finger between my seat and hers.

She lifted her brows and shook her head. Wise.

We stopped several more times for fuel and breaks. Kids ran into the marts and came out with bags of candy or donuts or chips and sodas. But while they were gone, I closed my eyes for a few precious minutes. I had no money. My bladder was not full of soda. So I dozed while they shopped and relieved themselves, and when they came back, I cried a little.

I was an old lady on a bus full of hooligans. We crawled along, dragging in the weather. I don't remember sleeping, but as we climbed mountains and minced down the far sides, I felt a great urgency to get to my family, my traditions, my decorations, my food, my house. As the sun rose, I counted my blessings, but I was very impatient about it.

At three o'clock in the afternoon, and to my shock, two full hours *ahead* of schedule, we finally arrived in Spokane. We were assured that the charter company had called the parent contacts and word had gotten to our families in time. As we unloaded, I could think only that in two and a half more hours I would be sipping hot cocoa with my siblings while listening to the Carpenters' Christmas album and winning at Pictionary. Outside with my backpack, duffle bag, and pillow, I searched for my grandparents, rejoicing to be off that hot, noisy, obnoxious vehicle. *Freshmen.*

I spotted my grandpa first—tall, in a pale-blue coat, with strawberry-blond hair mixed with silver beneath a light-gray fedora.

He opened his arms. "Hi, Kris." I returned his strong hug as Cassi and Sean found their parents. I waved goodbye, and we wished each other a merry Christmas.

I looked at the empty Chrysler as we approached. I'd expected my grandma to be sitting in the car, waiting out of the cold. "Where's Grandma?"

"Well, we thought you'd like to come to the house, get a bite to eat, maybe have a nap before the trip to your folks' house," Grandpa rather sheepishly explained.

A *nap*? A *bite to eat*? I wanted to *go*. I wanted to go home *now*. I wanted to shake my head and fold my arms and stomp a foot, but my grandpa was one of my favorite people, and I was not raised to be ungrateful. So I faked a smile. "Okay," I said. But I wanted to cry.

We drove the familiar streets to my grandparents' home, up the long climb of Spokane's South Hill, perforated by occasional "steps" to break up the steep incline. Grandpa always drove fast enough that we almost got air where the road abruptly flattened out. He grinned as I giggled and held my stomach, feeling like I was six years old.

We parked in the driveway of the only house I remembered my grandparents living in, although I knew their previous home was just down the street. That one was a 60s modern-style house with a flat roof, carport, and big windows. This house, though, was a California-split two-story, with gold-dimpled glass next to the front door and, beyond that, a set of stairs we kids had spent hours climbing up and sliding down.

I followed Grandpa to the front door, dismayed that he'd grabbed my bags to carry into the house. Why did I need my bags? I wouldn't need my bags.

The door opened before we got there, and my grandpa stood aside.

"Oh, Kris, you made it." I was greeted with hugs and kisses from Grandma and the smells of chicken, Aqua Net, Old Spice, and Christmas tree. "Welcome." She held me away to look me over, beaming with joy, her eyes a little glossy. My grandma's eyes always got a little glossy at homecomings.

I'd grown taller than her lately. Her thick, shiny, silver-white waves of hair were cut short and combed to perfection around her pretty face. Those big, bright eyes behind her glasses were mine.

I decided to relax and enjoy. After all, I was this far and already surrounded by love and the promise of warm food. What difference would one hour make?

Dinner was chicken and noodles over mashed potatoes. My grandparents are the only people I know who make homemade chicken and noodles and then take it one step further by pouring the savory stew over creamy mashed potatoes. After I ate my fill, I sat back with my belly full.

"How about that nap?" my grandpa asked.

"Oh . . . I could sleep in the car—"

"Oh, no," Grandma insisted. "That wouldn't be comfortable."

"We've got the bed. We've got the blankets," Grandpa said persuasively.

I would have argued further, but with the warm food and the long trip behind me, exhaustion reared its head and said, *Need sleep. Now.* I pushed my chair back, let myself be directed away from the dishes, and made my way back to the spare room.

In no time, I was asleep on the yellow satin coverlet, with one of Grandma's crocheted afghans pulled snugly over me. I slept hard. I don't know for how long. I started coming out of sleep as if I were climbing out of a well, reaching daylight, blinking my eyes.

And I thought I saw my dad staring at me.

I squeezed my eyes shut again. Great. I wanted so badly to see my family that I was conjuring them up right there in that room.

Then I heard a snicker, and my brother's voice whispering, "Didn't she look at you?"

My eyes flew open, and I sat up. No apparition stood before me. This was no dream. In my grandparents' spare room, watching me struggle between dreaming and waking, stood my family. My dad; my mom; my sister, Shelli; and my brothers, Mike and Craig; all grinned triumphantly at me.

I shrieked, and they laughed, and I cried. I looked again at my dad, his youthful face, his thick brown hair turning silver, his build and posture like mine, his grin at the good joke. They were so familiar to me, all of them. I knew these five people better than any others on earth.

"You know, you kind of messed things up for us, Krissi," Dad said with his quiet voice. He was the only person in the world allowed to call me Krissi.

"What?" I asked. "How?" I was just a pawn. A speck. A tumbleweed rolling across four states on a bus full of sleep-deprived, half-crazed, soda-high college students.

"We were going to surprise you at the bus stop—"

"But your bus got here early," my mom finished for him, her expression a mix of aggravation and delight. "Poor Grandpa had to cover for us while we made the trip as fast as we could."

I looked over at Grandpa, who joined us in the room.

"I'm sorry about that." He chuckled. "You know, Kris, you didn't fool me one bit. I don't think I've seen you that frustrated before."

I bit my lip and felt the flush of guilt come to my face. "Thanks for hanging in there with the surprise."

I looked around at my family. Craig dropped onto the bed, bouncing it a little. Mike shook his head at me, smiling as if I was such a dork. Shelli hugged my mom, beaming with the success of the surprise as my mom ran her hand over my nap hair. It was wonderful. Better than if they'd met me at the bus.

And I was struck with a realization: they'd missed me.

I was the big bossy sister, the first child to talk back, the first to rebel. The one to make up the rules and dole out the punishments. The one with the messy room and lame sense of humor, and I'd just assumed that it was enough for them that I would be coming home for Christmas sooner or later. But for my family, later was not enough. They'd rushed to see *me*. I was loved, cherished. Missed.

Later that night, in my home decorated for my Christmas, after eating my food with my family and after dropping into my bed—well, kind of my bed because I'd been moved to the loft (I guess they didn't miss me *that* much)—I wondered again at the realization that I wasn't the only one longing for my family. As I prayed that night, I considered our Heavenly Father, and once more I was struck. We live our lives making mistakes and blundering through and hoping we're good enough to be thought of and believing we're no big deal or we're dorks or just specks. And I considered how maybe, just maybe, on the other side of things, we are loved. We are cherished.

We are *missed*.

And that realization made that Christmas the sweetest one I'd had yet and worth any kind of journey home.

OTHER BOOKS BY KRISTA LYNNE JENSEN

Of Grace and Chocolate

The Orchard

Falling for You

With All My Heart

Kisses in the Rain

HAND-DRAWN MARSHMALLOWS AND OTHER CHRISTMAS MIRACLES

BY MEG JOHNSON

I cried the hardest my first Christmas in a wheelchair. I'm not saying that because this is a Christmas story or because I am trying to milk some emotions. It really was the hardest time for me that year. I had been paralyzed in a hiking accident that March and released from the hospital in June—*released* was the word they used, but I was, from that time on, wheelchair *bound.* My legs wouldn't move. My stomach and back muscles didn't work. And my hands were lifeless and floppy.

The whole year was hard, don't get me wrong, but Christmas brought a whole new level of challenges. I have a small family, but we are big on creativity, so for Christmas, we were all over the handmade cards, hand-crafted candy, hand-painted . . . stuff. It was all about the handmade, but the trouble was, my lifeless and floppy hands didn't work.

I sat by myself with a tube of wrapping paper, some tape, and a store-bought gift in a small box. I refused help from everyone; I wanted to do it myself. And all by myself. I had lost so much independence being paralyzed that I fought for every morsel I could get. It must have been an hour of ripping (scissors were out of the question; how could I use those with no finger movement?) and taping. The result was a tape-covered, squished ball of Christmas paper. Independence isn't always beautiful.

Everyone said I should be proud as they set it under the tree next to the other gifts tied with multilooped ribbons, glittery craft sticks, and origami birds. That was seriously how my family wrapped their gifts.

After that initial Christmas disappointment, I worked hard the next year and, one by one, relearned to how to tape and tie and use scissors (cue the Hallelujah chorus). By the next Christmas, I was wrapping gifts almost as beautifully and just as independently as I'd done before my accident.

And I was regaining more independence in other areas of my life too. That very next Christmas, I drove myself to the Ross department store in Centerville, Utah. There was a light snow, and I was going Christmas shopping . . . by myself! It was my very first time driving alone anywhere at all since I'd been paralyzed. At first it took a long time to get myself, meaning my ragdoll body, into the car, so people always had to help me and were always, always with me. But I found a car I could put my wheelchair in and lift myself into, and after a long, hard road (no pun intended) of test drives and a whole lot of practice, I learned to drive it with the use of hand controls.

As I drove to Ross to shop by myself, my heart soared in the sheer indescribable feeling of regained independence. Truly, I don't know how to describe it, but I think you can slightly compare it to the feeling you'd have if you grew so big that you could step off the earth, turn around, and hold it in your hand.

As I got out of my car and into my wheelchair at Ross, the tiny snowflakes felt like congratulatory kisses on my face.

I slammed the door shut in total triumph. I raised both my hands into the air and exclaimed victoriously, "I'm alone!"

My enthusiasm must have frightened some passing shoppers because an elderly couple stopped to see if I was okay. They were very concerned and offered to stay with me since I was apparently "alone." I hadn't realized that maybe some little girl in a wheelchair in the snow, staring at her car and shouting, might need a little supervision.

My car became my passport to anything I ever wanted. Anywhere. I felt so liberated. Wheelchair bound now meant only that I couldn't stand, not that I couldn't move.

And I was on the go. I went back to college. I joined the wheelchair rugby team. I competed at Ms. Wheelchair America. I got married!

My husband, Whit Johnson, was a former boyfriend who heard about my accident and visited me in the hospital several times. After I was released from the hospital, he drove me to therapy and took me to young single adult activities and firesides. We watched movies together and talked. And then he proposed to me late one night in October with pumpkins he'd carved to say, "Meg, will you marry me?"

A few weeks before we were married, Whit and I were sitting on the couch watching a movie. We held hands but not really. My paralyzed fingers just flailed. I pushed our hands into the black leather of the couch so my fingers would wrap around his, but as I did, my heart sank. What kind of subpar wife was I going to be? I couldn't even hold his hand. How could I do the other things wives did? I couldn't believe he was going to marry me. Surely he deserved someone better. Someone more able.

I looked up to him and asked, "Doesn't it bother you that I can't walk?" I knew it did. How could it not?

He was quiet for a few moments before he responded. "Yes," he said. "But not as much as it would if I couldn't be with you."

My husband married me as I was, wheelchair and all, on February 29, 2008, four years after I was paralyzed. We were sealed in the Salt Lake Temple for time and all eternity—and they don't make wheelchairs in eternity.

I know we're not your normal couple, but really, who is? Everyone has disabilities they work through and weaknesses they are trying to overcome. In that respect we're not that different from any other couple. We just pretend like I'm not in a wheelchair, and it really doesn't seem like I am. We try to do things the normal way. My husband works and fixes stuff in our home. I make breakfast, dinner, and sometimes lunch. I visit teach as well as do laundry, and we take Christmas gifts to the neighbors.

My husband likes to adopt the idea that you don't want to miss somebody, so you probably shouldn't take gifts to anybody. That way nobody feels left out. I like to take the stance that if you give a gift to every single person in the entire neighborhood and surrounding streets, you don't miss anybody.

Needless to say, my husband thinks I overdo it. I think he might be right, but that still doesn't stop me. I love being able to show a little love for my ward family and neighbors by giving them something I've made.

We were still essentially newlyweds the Christmas I decided to make small marshmallow treats for the neighbors. When I say marshmallow "treats," I really just mean marshmallows. I'm not a very fancy baker like all the amazing Pinterest wives, but I am pretty artsy, and I like to draw, so I drew small Christmas pictures on each marshmallow with edible markers.

My pictures weren't Rembrandts, but each one took me several minutes. To draw, I wove the edible marker between the fingers of one hand and held the marshmallow up with the other. The pictures were small, so I had to hold them close to my face so I could see what I was doing, but because my tummy and back muscles don't work, I was merely balancing my upper body in place while I drew each picture. I didn't want to move and ruin the drawings, so I had to hold my breath as I flexed all the rest of the working muscles in my shoulders, neck, and face so I could create these mini edible masterpieces.

I had about five marshmallows in each bag and over forty bags, so it was a lot of breath holding and breaks. But I got them all done and wrapped them up in Christmas bags with Christmas bows. I was so pleased with myself. I mean, there weren't any glitter sticks or origami birds, but I'd done them myself, and they looked pretty dang decent.

It was a cold night a few days before Christmas when my husband was loading all of our marshmallow treat bags into my Subaru Baja for delivery. We had plenty of snow, and it seemed like the perfect Christmas night to deliver our hand-drawn Christmas treats to our neighbors. My husband had turned on the car and turned up the heat so it would be nice and warm for me when I got in, which was nice because something weird about being in a wheelchair is that I cannot control my temperature. It was actually the first ability to go when I broke my neck. I just stopped being able to sweat or warm up my body. I can't control it at all; whatever the weather is around me is what my body tries to be. I am literally cold blooded. So my husband was trying to make it easy for me so I could go from my warm house to my warm car and not be chilled while we delivered our special gifts.

When everything was finally loaded (and hopefully not melting in the full-blast heat), my husband came back in for me. We did not want or need to bring my wheelchair along, so he was going to pick me up and put me on his back, piggy-back style.

I kind of love to ride on his back and remember what it feels like to step and move with legs beneath me. I also like to see from his viewpoint. I'm so short, I don't get the visual standing people get. However, maybe that's not such a bad thing because when he picks me up, it reminds me that I need to dust. Sometimes ignorance is bliss.

Anyway, my husband opened the front door wide so we could walk out once he picked me up, but as he did so, he saw our car, our nice warm car with all the Christmas bow-tied hand-drawn marshmallow gifts, driving down our quiet neighborhood street. Without us.

Time seemed to stand still. Then, in slow motion, my husband turned to me, his eyes as wide as the distance between us and our car, and said, "Our car's been stolen."

Our car. *My* car. The only car I could drive. The only car that could fit my wheelchair. My passport to the outside world. My element of independence had been taken. It was long gone in the dark December night.

And so were all of the hand-drawn marshmallow gifts.

The open door let in a Christmas chill as my husband and I stared at each other, neither one of us daring to look away, or daring to even blink, both searching for some explanation, some rationale, but finding nothing except what surely was a mirrored image of our own wide-eyed, disbelieving look.

We were on the verge of tears, and we knew it, but before any could fall, I quickly said, "We can cry, or we can laugh, but there's no going back."

So we laughed. And we laughed hard. And we laughed so hard we cried.

We had a hard time calling the police because they didn't take our call very seriously. We just kept laughing. They kept asking if it was a joke. Yes, we supposed it was, but the joke was on the thieves who probably don't even need a wheelchair-accessible car. Or hand-drawn marshmallows.

Our car being stolen was quite the Christmas sensation. Our families, our friends, and the entire community was in an uproar. The newspaper headlines read:

"Thief Steals Woman's Specially Modified Car"

"Grinch Steals Paralyzed Woman's Specially Modified Car in Ogden"

"Grinch Steals Disabled Woman's Car and All Her Handmade Gifts"

We got phone calls, e-mails, and letters from friends, family, and strangers whose hearts went out to us that Christmas. Our names were put on multiple temple prayer rolls. Facebook exploded with people sharing in the loss of the car and my independence.

My husband and I continued laughing through it all. Our newlywed salary didn't give us a lot of options except to just start saving our pennies for another wheelchair-accessible car.

That Christmas we adopted my husband's philosophy that if you don't give any of your neighbors gifts, nobody feels left out.

Late into the night on Christmas Eve, Whit and I cuddled close on the couch. We were sure Santa Claus couldn't fit a new car, or any other element of independence, into our stockings, but we enjoyed the flashing lights on the tree.

My husband squeezed me tight and said he was glad I hadn't been in the car. I squeezed him right back and said

I was glad *he* hadn't been in the car. We both agreed that they could take the car, the independence, the treats, the time, and the effort, but there was nothing in the car we would miss this Christmas.

It was okay that our car, my car, had been taken. As I laid my head on my husband's chest and felt him breathe in and out as he fell asleep, I thought about how hard I'd fought to do things on my own. I thought about how triumphant I'd felt when I could finally drive by myself. I thought about how happy I'd been when I could finally tape things and use scissors.

But wrapping a beautiful present, complete with glitter sticks and origami birds, didn't seem like the goal anymore as I snuggled closer to my husband. After all, independence isn't the plan. It never was. We weren't sent to earth to see how much we could do all by ourselves but, rather, to see how well we shared the gifts we brought with us and how well we unwrapped the gifts we see in each other. And to see how much we could rely on God.

I must have dozed off with my husband, enveloped in the light of the Christmas tree, because we were both startled by a late-night phone call from "Officer Elf" informing us that the police had found our car.

Three big, tough men were driving it along Main Street when a canine unit pulled them over. The three men jumped out and ran like crazy to try to get away, but the dog caught one of the men and dragged him to the ground.

The police returned the car to us that night, complete with brass knuckles, but not any hand-drawn marshmallow treats. We like to think the thieves ate them.

We resumed cuddling on the couch and laughed once again as we considered the past few days. We laughed at the car, the newspaper headlines, the worry, the brass knuckles.

We laughed and hugged and hugged some more. And as we hugged, it suddenly occurred to me that no matter what abilities I had or didn't have, no matter how fancy my bows were or whether I could add glitter sticks to my presents, I was sealed to my husband for time and all eternity, and that was a gift no one could steal.

And I don't need scissors, glitter sticks, or tape to wrap him tightly in—just my arms to hold him close this Christmas . . . and the eternity of Christmases to come.

OTHER BOOKS BY MEG JOHNSON

When Life Gets Hard

Always a Princess

THE PERFECT GIFT

BY MELANIE JACOBSON

When I was a kid, we had a lot of Christmases where we didn't get much in the way of presents. My parents both had stable jobs as teachers, but medical bills for my dad wreaked regular havoc on our budget, and Christmases were a luxury we often trimmed back. We didn't mind. We always got something.

Around the time I was in middle school, our fortunes changed. My dad's health had been okay for a while, the hospital bills had all been paid off, and more presents piled up beneath the tree at Christmastime. It wasn't a hard thing to get used to, and we liked it: lots of shredded wrapping paper followed by haphazard stacks of all the things we'd asked for in front of us.

We had another lean year when I was in high school and my dad lost his job, but then it went back to normal again—traditions and Christmas food, family and friends, putting together the Christmas tree, and opening gifts on Christmas morning.

Christmas took on a different meaning when I left home for BYU. After spending a whole semester living off of Rice-a-Roni and pinching pennies, it was nice to come home and grab things out of the fridge whenever I wanted, and opening presents on Christmas morning felt like the purest indulgence. Stuff just to have stuff? I loved the sense of security that came with being a little spoiled by my parents for that one day.

And then came the Christmas where it all got upended by someone who had just the wrong combination of intelligence and laziness. It's a complicated tale involving fraud, big business, and cold, cold calculation.

A few days before I was supposed to come home from BYU for Christmas break during my sophomore year, I got a call from my dad. This was always a big deal because my parents were deaf. To call me, he first had to call a relay operator, who would then call me. Next, my dad would type into a machine called a TTY, and the operator would read his message to me. I would respond, and the operator would type my message back to my dad. It wasn't the easiest way to have a conversation, so generally when my dad called, he had something specific in mind. I wasn't quite worried because every now and then he would make up a reason to call me just as a pretext so we could communicate in those pre-email days. But I was definitely on high alert.

Even without hearing his actual tone, frustration underlined all of his words the operator read to me. "Wanted to let you know that we've been robbed, and it's going to take a while to get everything straightened out. Someone forged the check we wrote for car insurance and cashed it."

The thing is, my parents paid their insurance for all three vehicles twice a year, so the check was for over $700. Someone had painstakingly altered the line where it said whom the check was written to and had instead filled in the name of a toy store. The note on the memo line read "Kids Christmas."

Hindsight makes me grateful that in our family, presents were only a bonus at Christmastime and never the point. My parents would never have dreamed of stealing to make it happen. Christmas could still be Christmas in our home without gifts, and as it turned out, that year that was exactly how it would have to be.

As someone barely out of her teens, I was beyond frustrated, not by the lack of gifts but by the unfairness of the thievery.

"We won't be able to do much as far as gifts go," my dad told me.

It turned out that the perpetrator worked in the insurance company's regional office. She'd been caught, and the bank was already aware that my parents had been fraud victims. The money was eventually returned, but it took weeks to get it all sorted out. In the meantime, my parents paid the insurance company again, another $700, to make sure the cars stayed insured. That was where the designated Christmas money—and then some!—had disappeared to.

What was more, my dad explained, tithing settlements were approaching. "We could use that money for Christmas and then catch up with our tithing in January when they resolve everything at the bank, but your mom and I want you to know that we never considered that option. We want to pay the Lord first. We can do delayed Christmas presents in January. We'll make sure to ship you something at school."

My dad was never one to give a lot of gifts, and the ones he gave were terrible, but they were so carefully considered that I could only love them. Many years later, when I moved back in with them for a time, I mentioned that my room, a converted garage, was often drafty. That year, for my thirtieth birthday, he bought me tubes of caulk. He was delighted with himself. In his opinion, it was the best gift he could give me: a lesson in caulking so I could fix problems like this in the future for myself. On another Christmas, he gave me plastic hooks for my bedroom wall. It seemed he thought the reason I always had clothes all over my floor was because I needed more places to hang things.

I promised him that I understood about the delayed Christmas and had no problem with it, but when I got home for the Christmas break a week or so later, I could tell the sparseness beneath the tree bothered him. My dad had been an educator his whole life, and his deafness limited the number of places he could teach. He'd taken a job in LA that kept him away from his family five days a week solely to provide for us, and it weighed on him that he wouldn't be able to give us gifts. But he was sure that paying tithing and waiting on the Lord was the right thing to do, even with the bare space beneath our tree.

I don't remember even one of us three kids being upset with my parents for this choice. My youngest sister was fifteen, and we'd witnessed my parents' faithfulness and obedience for so many years that we wouldn't have expected anything less. We were frustrated by the person who had felt stealing from my parents was the best way to take care of her own Christmas, but we kept our frustrations to ourselves and focused on our other traditions. We made my dad's special queso dip that can only be served from Thanksgiving to New Year's. We rented movies and popped popcorn on the stovetop, drenching it in enough butter to float it out to sea. And we waited for my dad to finish out the last week of school before Christmas break so he could come home and make it really feel like Christmas at last.

He finished on a Friday. I expected him to come home looking tired and ready to drag me to the sofa for a *Star*

Trek marathon. Instead, he called all of us kids together and sat us down.

"On Sunday, your mom and I went in for our tithing settlement and handed the bishop the money that could have saved Christmas. We declared ourselves full tithe payers, and we had no regrets. Today as I was walking out to catch a ride back out of LA with my coworker, I felt a strong prompting to check my teacher mailbox. I'd already checked it a little earlier, and it had been empty, and I didn't feel like holding up my carpool buddy by walking all the way back to the office. But the prompting came again, so I asked her to wait, and I went back to my mailbox. There was a new envelope in it, and when I opened it, there was a check for some back pay the district owed us from contract negotiations."

He smiled then, leaning forward to tell us the best part of the story. "The amount of the check is almost the exact amount that was stolen from us. We didn't pay our tithing because we thought the Lord would save Christmas. We did it to be obedient. But I know the timing of this check and the prompting to go back and check an empty mailbox that I wouldn't see again for three weeks was the Lord's way of rewarding that obedience. So Christmas presents are on again. Give me your lists!"

There were presents that year. But I don't remember a single one. Instead, I remember the gift my dad gave us that sticks with me still: an example of faith and obedience.

I've experienced many Christmases since then and opened presents that will hold a special place in my home for the rest of my life, but my dad's gift that year has become a permanent part of me, woven into the fabric of who I am. At times when I have struggled with my faith, this is one of those touchstone moments I come back to, a small miracle that can't be explained by coincidence, only by the kindness of a loving Heavenly Father. And so my father did it again: he found me a gift that is exactly what I need.

OTHER BOOKS BY MELANIE JACOBSON

Twitterpated

The List

Second Chances

Not My Type

Smart Move

Painting Kisses

Always Will

Southern Charmed

TIME, TALENTS, AND THE TWINKLE STAR (A STORY WITHIN A STORY)

BY PAMELA CARRINGTON REID

Satin . . . velvet . . . cotton . . . My hands quickly ran over the bolts of bright-toned and differently patterned fabric. Years of experience with sewing told me I would know which fabrics I needed as soon as I touched them. And right now, I had to do a lot of touching to prepare for all the Christmas gifts I was going to make in the next few weeks.

I had just added another bolt to my cart when I heard the voice behind the shelves, a little high-pitched and strained.

"I really don't know what I need, dear. Can you help me?"

The sales assistant's voice was less audible in response, but then I had to turn as the first voice became more desperate . . . and recognizable.

"I just know I have to get this fixed, somehow, for Christmas."

She was a lady from church, and in an instant, as I listened, I knew that if I turned the corner, I was going to walk straight into another project I seriously didn't need right now.

"I . . . I just don't know where to start."

Almost wishing I'd come shopping earlier in the day, I hesitated, then, with a deep breath, I pushed my cart around the fixture. "Carol, can I help?"

It was like watching Christmas lights come on as Carol turned and her face lit up. "Oh, Pamela! You know all about sewing! Do you think you can?" She held up a dilapidated Santa doll, the clothes worn and torn, and the beard matted and wispy. "This was Jim's when he was a little boy, and it's very special, and now we have our first grandchild coming, and I know he'd like to have it for her, but I haven't got a clue how to make it look better or where to start . . . and I just want Jim to be happy. It's been hard."

I had met Carol's husband, Jim, a few times at social gatherings—a lovely man—and as she held out the doll, I could suddenly imagine him holding it as a little boy.

I also knew that as soon as I touched that doll, I was committed. Thoughts of all my other projects and deadlines raced through my head. I really didn't have time for this!

My fingers felt the thin fabric.

"You know, Carol, I just saw the exact red velvet over there." I pointed behind me. "And the white fur is over there . . ."

* * *

It actually didn't take long to make Santa's red cloak, and the new moustache and beard seemed to breathe life into him. As I held it out in front of me, I knew it would make both Carol and Jim happy, but then as I stared at the doll, I noticed the very faint outline of a star in both eyes.

It was late as I began to search through my craft box for the tube of white paint.

And it was somewhere between painting the first star into the left eye and beginning the right eye that I had "the story" come to me.

Now, I loved to write but had often doubted whether anyone would actually want to read anything I'd written, and therefore, I wondered if it was all a waste of time—time I usually filled with sewing projects so I didn't have to think about writing.

But this story was so clear in my mind I knew I had to write it . . . for Jim.

In the early hours of the morning, I finally printed off the story and attached it as a scroll to the Santa doll. Once again, I felt a sudden rush of doubt that Carol and Jim would even want the story. They only needed the Santa doll.

But I had to admit it gave me a thrill to hand it all to Carol the next day with a quick explanation as to how the story had evolved as well as the new Santa.

The greatest joy came that evening when Carol called. "It's perfect, Pamela. Jim was so emotional when he saw the doll, but when he read the story"—I heard her voice catch—"he said that that was exactly as it happened, and he's just so, so grateful that the twinkle star is back. Thank you so much."

I've forgotten all of the other Christmas gifts I made that year, but I've never forgotten the Santa doll or the joy I found when I took time to really give.

And if you're wondering about the story . . .

The Twinkle Star
by Pamela Carrington Reid

He was a fine Santa! The thick wool of his beard tumbled down over his belly in shiny, creamy curls. His dark-red hood and cloak were rich and velvety to the touch, and the fur trim was warm and fluffy.

Young Jim's fingers slowly explored the Santa doll, enjoying the wonder of it. Then he stopped, his eyes searching Santa's face—rosy, pink cheeks and a round, red nose shone above his bushy moustache. Laughing lips peeped out from underneath the full beard.

But Jim couldn't stop looking at Santa's eyes—bright eyes in shades of blue, and they twinkled! Twinkled because of the shining star painted onto each eye. Jim carefully touched the eyes, then he felt his own eyelids. Did his eyes have twinkling stars, or was it only Santa's? How did you get a twinkly star in your eyes?

At dinner, Mother carefully placed the Santa doll in the middle of the table. He looked so fine that even the poor meal of beans, potatoes, and sausages looked extra special. Santa watched Jim and his family eat, and the twinkle never left his eye.

After dinner, Mother had another surprise. Jim could hardly believe his eyes when she lifted the corner of Santa's red cloak. Christmas crackers! The children were overjoyed as they each took a cracker; it was as if Santa himself was giving the gift.

Jim was sure Santa's eyes were sparkling even more. Christmas was so special that year.

And the years passed . . .

Every Christmas, Jim would wait impatiently for the Santa doll to be brought out at dinner. The other children were eager to get their crackers, but Jim watched for Santa's eyes. Yes, the twinkle was still there. He would touch the laughing face and wonder if his own eyes would ever sparkle like Santa's.

Every year the doll stood in the middle of the Christmas table, tall and smiling, putting the sparkle into their meal.

Every year, the Christmas meal was bigger and better and the other decorations brighter and shinier.

And the years passed . . .

One year, when Jim was no longer young, he sat down to Christmas dinner and noticed that the fancy plates all had a large red-and-gold Christmas cracker beside them. But there was no Santa doll on the table. Jim looked around the room. The Santa doll stood silently on a small table in the corner.

His handsome red cloak looked dull and faded next to the bright-red decorations. The fur trim was worn on the edges where young hands had tugged back the cloak to find their Christmas crackers. The curly white beard was thinner and matted and hung limply.

And his eyes . . . Jim stared. The twinkle had almost gone, worn off by little fingers. The blue eyes looked darker and more lonely without the star shining in them. Jim shrugged and turned to grab his larger, brighter Christmas cracker with his brother.

The next year, the Santa doll lay in its box right through Christmas. And the next year, Jim went away.

And many, many years passed . . .

Old Jim rocked quietly by the heater, spreading his hands to its meager warmth. He wasn't sure if he liked Christmas anymore. All the children lived so far away. He didn't like being ill . . . or old . . . or alone.

"I feel just like that old Santa doll." Old Jim shook his head and breathed a long sigh. "He lost the sparkle in his eye, and finally nobody wanted him either." A single tear slid down his round, pink cheek and buried itself in his snowy-white moustache. He closed his eyes and, stroking his bushy beard, remembered Christmases long ago.

"Surprise! Surprise, Grandpa! We're here for Christmas!" Young James, the littlest grandson, threw himself into his grandfather's arms, closely followed by his brothers and sisters and mother.

"And look, Dad, I have a surprise for you and the children. I found this Santa doll in the attic in an old box." His daughter, Natalie, smiled as she opened a large bag, then held out the Santa doll.

"He looked all old and dusty, so I made him new clothes and a new white beard, and now he looks just fine."

Grandpa Jim's shaking fingers explored the Santa doll. It did look splendid with a new fluffy white beard and rich red velvet cloak, but his eyes were fixed on Santa's face. The rosy cheeks seemed rosier. The laughing lips seemed even happier than he remembered. And the eyes . . . shades of bright blue . . . and how they twinkled! Twinkled because of the white star in each eye.

"I just had to paint the star back in. I remembered your stories about him when you were little." Natalie put her arm around his shoulders. "It was such a little thing to put the twinkle back in his eyes." She pointed to the cloak. "Do you want to show the children Santa's surprise?"

Grandpa Jim nodded happily as he slowly got up off his chair and placed the Santa doll on the table, then, with hands that trembled, he lifted the cloak.

The grandchildren gasped! Christmas crackers in bright gold and red!

Then they all eagerly reached for a cracker, except his youngest grandson.

Young James stared hard at the Santa's face, then reached tiny hands to the eyes and touched them very carefully. He turned to his grandfather. "Look, Grandpa, the Santa's eyes are shining . . . just like yours are. They've got stars in them."

Grandpa Jim wiped away a happy star tear and gave Young James a very big hug. "That's because it only takes a little thing to put the twinkle star back in your eye."

OTHER BOOKS BY

PAMELA CARRINGTON REID

Cliff Hanger

Coffin House

Remember No More

Small Grain of Sand

Safe Harbor

Shades of Gray

Little One

Something Familiar

A VERY BRAZILIAN CHRISTMAS

BY SANDRA GREY

Sister Ribeiro woke early Christmas morning, even before companionship study, and baked a cake, its smell floating us up out of our bunks.

Sister Ribeiro's chocolate cakes were to die for, and she had such a giving nature that almost every preparation day we transported on chocolaty waves all the way to heaven.

"*Obrigada*, Sister Ribeiro, you're the best!" My other companion, Sister Silva, reached for the dessert.

Sister Ribeiro swatted her hand. "Someone else is going to need this cake today."

"I need it!"

"Silva, hands off."

"It's not for us?"

"Not this time. Someone needs to know they're not alone today."

"*I'm* lonely."

Sister Ribeiro rolled her eyes.

"The elders?"

"Are you kidding? They wouldn't appreciate it. They'd just inhale it and demand more. It's for someone who really needs it."

"Who?"

Sister Ribeiro shrugged.

"You don't know who it's for?"

"We can pray and decide together who it's for."

We left the cake on the table in our kitchen, carefully packaged in a recycled *Panettone* box. We had our companionship study, our personal study, and our breakfast and then prepared to leave the apartment, all to the theme of chocolate-scented air. It was pure torture.

We gathered our bicycles and folded our arms in prayer.

Sister Silva did the honors. "Please, dear Lord, bless us that we might make a difference in someone's Christmas Day. We are so grateful for Thee, and for Thy Son, and we *so* want to make this a day with *purpose*."

I could feel the explosion ready to happen. We managed a pseudo-reverent "amen" before Sisters Silva and Ribeiro both burst out laughing.

"Not fair!" I swung my shoulder bag in a wide sweep at them. "That happened a lifetime ago!"

"You'll never live it down, Sister. Never!"

"I was a greenie," I defended myself against their hearty mirth. "I was in a hurry. I looked up the wrong word in my English/Portuguese dictionary. I misspelled the English word, that's all!"

"The bishop tells everybody about it! Every time he has missionaries over, he—"

"All right!" I laughed. "*Purpose*. *Porpoise*. You're never gonna let me live it down, are you?"

We bicycled to the church on what was cooking up to be a scorching day and met up with the other companionships in our district, parking our bikes in a secure location and going inside. We found a large classroom and sat in a circle.

"Dear elders and sisters," the eager, fresh-faced district leader from Wyoming began. "I know this is a different Christmas experience for many of us, whether we're from Brazil or from somewhere else. We all have things we miss; we all have Christmas traditions we aren't going to experience this year, loved ones we won't get to see . . . Why don't we each share something we really miss this Christmas." He smiled expectantly at all of us, encouraging us to share.

There was a pause. "A Christmas tree?" someone finally offered.

"Good!" the district leader encouraged.

"Presents."

"*Papai Noel.*"

Someone giggled. "Mistletoe."

"My mom's gingerbread."

The mention of Mom brought about a rapid evolution from inanimate objects to family.

"Mom's apple pie."

"Mom and Dad."

"My four-year-old sister."

"Caroling with family."

"Reading the Christmas story with my family."

Little by little, the circle of missionaries opened up in short, heartfelt responses.

"*Otimo*!" The district leader beamed, then took the feeling in the room and built upon it. "Sure, we don't have our parents or siblings here, our extended family or close friends, but who can tell me what we *do* have?"

"Companions."

"Scriptures."

"Mission family."

"The Savior."

"Investigators we love."

"*Sim*!" he agreed and happily tied our answers into his prepared message. "We are here to serve the Lord, and even though we miss some things about our Christmases before our missions, our Christmas is filled with the things that are most important at this time in our lives and in the lives of our investigators."

He leaned forward, moving toward the crux of his message. "As representatives of Jesus Christ, we can focus on those things that are most important. This afternoon we have an opportunity to touch many lives; we can bless those investigators we visit with a message befitting this Christmas Day; when we go out to work, we should take a moment to decide as companionships what the true purpose of Christmas is!"

Our district leader was new to Praia Grande. He'd spent most of his mission in Santo Andre and had just recently transferred to the Baixada. I, on the other hand, had the unique distinction of being one of the very few missionaries *ever* to have transferred back to the same area in which I'd been trained. Same area, same ward, same apartment, even the same bicycle.

Several of the missionaries were new, but there were enough still present who remembered my blunder. My companions hadn't been my companions when it had happened, but Sister Ribeiro had been here. And Sister Silva had heard about it through the grapevine. Several sisters began giggling, the sound beginning behind hands clapped tightly over mouths and then swelling into general mirth.

The poor district leader looked up from his notes, first confused, then embarrassed. "What?" he demanded, and the laughter really began to roll.

"Sure, rub it in!" I hissed, embarrassed but laughing all the same.

"What did I say?" the district leader demanded.

When we went outside, it felt more like the Fourth of July than Christmas. We barbecued sausages and steak in ninety-degree weather with almost the same degree of humidity. Some of us played basketball, pounding the concrete with a dilapidated ball some former missionary had left in the janitorial closet.

The heat sapped the energy right out of us, but that was one of the most memorable get-togethers of my mission. Many of us lay on our backs in the coarse grass and sparse shade to read letters from family and friends, letters that had arrived a few days before at our zone conference. Some we had saved specially for this day.

I missed my family and many family Christmas traditions, it was true, but our district leader was exactly right; the things that mattered most were right here with us in the mission field.

My companions and I agreed that we wanted that Christmas to be extra special. Sister Silva, Sister Ribeiro, and I hurried home and changed into proselyting clothes. We grabbed several copies of the Book of Mormon and our bound discussions, and Sister Ribeiro carefully strapped the box with her cake in it to the back of her bike.

She touched my arm. "This might be your last area, Sister, and I wanted to make Christmas unforgettable for you also."

"Oh, Sister Ribeiro, there's no way I can forget!"

"I just wanted to give you something, something to remember your time here, remember our companionship; you, Silva, me . . ."

"How about your cake recipe?"

She laughed. "*Tudo bem*. But I want it to be something more." She hesitated and, for just a moment, looked mildly worried. "You know I wouldn't tease you if you couldn't take it, don't you?"

"Of course."

"Then you aren't mad at us for laughing about what happened last time you were here?"

"Not at all." I grinned. "I deserve it. And I understand there are worse mistakes a greenie just learning Portuguese can make."

"And I've probably heard them all." Ribeiro laughed. "I just wanted to know"—she sobered—"because the last time we were at the *feira* on the beach, I bought something for you."

She held out a tiny package wrapped in brown paper and twine. "Open it!"

I untied the twine and carefully removed the brown paper, then opened the small box. Inside was a pair of earrings. Each portrayed a miniature figurine carved out of silver, flying upward out of small silver waves—two tiny marine porpoises.

Laughing, I put the earrings on and hugged my diminutive companion.

We bowed our heads, and it was my turn to offer a short prayer. I asked for help to touch people's hearts. I asked for protection and inspiration. And then I added, "And please help us find the right person for Sister Ribeiro's cake."

Sister Ribeiro balanced her bicycle and its chocolate cake down three flights of stairs and out of the apartment building, and then we headed southwest along the *Avenida Presidente Castello Branco*, pedaling parallel to the beach. Christmas had brought its fair share of tourists from the Sao Paulo megalopolis, and the road was congested to the point that, other than feet, a bicycle was the only form of reliable transportation.

I could see the worry on Sister Ribeiro's face as we dodged traffic. Her hand reached often to steady the box on the back of her bicycle. She'd worked hard on that cake, and I found myself mouthing a quick prayer on its behalf.

After the Sao Paulo Telecommunications building, we were finally able to abandon the *Avenida*. We turned northward toward the *Rua Pedro Cabal*. Then it was southwest again until we could turn in the direction of the *Praca Xavier*. Now the beach with all its beach bodies, rock music, and alcohol was finally out of sound, smell, and sight. The trip became almost peaceful, free from all the worldly craziness that accompanied Christmas Day in Brazil.

But the roads were now primarily cobblestone, and as our bicycles danced, Sister Ribeiro went into cardiac arrest. She had one hand permanently on her box and the other holding a handlebar.

We stopped to visit a recently baptized member at his food cart.

He brought out a plate of *pasteis*, or fried pastries. "Eat, sisters!"

"*Irmao* Sanchez, we can't!"

"Of course you can. Eat!"

We each ate a *pastel* dripping sinful meat juice and emitting all sorts of beautiful smells.

"You eat almost nothing," Sanchez accused. "Eat more."

"We're so stuffed; we couldn't possibly."

"Eat more!"

"Okay . . ."

I glanced over at Sister Ribeiro. She caught the question in my eyes and looked at the cake box. She thought a moment and then shook her head.

"*Irmao*, we want to sing for you and your customers. Something special for Christmas." We sang "Silent Night," the only Christmas song we had practiced together and the only one I could sing from memory in Portuguese. Pedestrians heard us singing and approached the cart. Several people stayed to listen and then bought *pasteis*. Our convert was so happy that he offered us more food.

We wished Sanchez a wonderful Christmas and escaped toward the plaza.

Cobblestones transitioned into dirt, and the bicycles took the brunt of the conversion. Sister Ribeiro moaned as her bicycle shook. We passed boys in the street playing soccer with a tin can. Scrawny boys dressed in nothing but shorts and an occasional T-shirt kicked the can around in front of the neighborhood convenience store. They'd shed their flip-flops for the occasion and were now engaged in the most intense game of barefoot soccer ever, dodging in and out of the occasional automobile's path, kicking up dust along with the can, laughing, yelling. Their feet moved as if in a Brazilian version of an Irish River Dance, sometimes so fast the tangle of legs was an unfollowable blur. The can was constantly moving, dancing, bouncing from one dirty foot to the next, seldom touching the ground and seldom slowing.

It stopped as someone put a foot on it. "It's the sisters! *Deixa-los passer!* Let them pass!"

"*Feliz Natal*, Sisters!"

"Merry Christmas to you as well!"

At least one of the boys had to be a member of our small ward. But they were all so covered in street dirt that it was hard to determine which. Their grins exposed the only dustless real estate on their bodies—their teeth.

"Sisters! *Feliz Natal*, Sisters!"

From his voice, we recognized the Da Silva boy. "Merry Christmas, Raymundo! Tell your mother hello!"

We continued west in the direction of the municipal school. It didn't take long to arrive at Senhor de Castro's residence. We'd found him the week previous and had already had one turbulent discussion with the man. He was Roman Catholic. His mother had been Catholic and his grandmother before her. But he liked our messages, he liked us, and he liked to compare religions. We still held out hope for him.

We left our bikes by the front door. Sister Ribeiro hesitated, her hand on the cake box. Then she reached for her scriptures. Her cake box stayed lashed to her bike.

We shared a special message about Jesus's birth and sang "Silent Night."

"Ha!" de Castro challenged. "That's a *Catholic* carol!"

Next we decided to visit a single mother with three small children. She had agreed to meet with us a couple of weeks ago but had missed her appointment. In order to get to Senhora Gomes's house in the *favela* slums, we had to cut through an alley to sidestep the beginnings of an alcohol-fueled street celebration, hike three blocks north, cross the *Avenida Presidente Kennedy*, and carry our bikes over a wooden bridge. This particular footbridge was constructed by merging two narrow planks with wire and an occasional rusty nail. The resulting structure spanned a moss-choked, garbage-strewn, foul-smelling canal filled with water, green foam, and sewage that looked like it had been fermenting since World War II.

In the past, we'd made a habit of conquering the narrow expanse on our bikes at full speed. We'd flown over this particular bridge so many times that we seldom even thought of the dire consequences that awaited us if the bridge twisted or a tire slipped even a fraction of an inch. But a greenie sister's fall and face-plant in the muck a few weeks before had caused us to reflect on our own mortality, and now we crossed the bridge carefully on foot.

On the opposite bank, we mounted our bikes and rode up the rutted street. Raw sewage ran in miniature rivers down the slope toward the canal. Our bicycles wove in and out of foot traffic headed south toward the beach. By now the cake was rattling around in its box, and Sister Ribeiro was practically weeping.

"We're giving it to Senhora Gomes!" she determined and gripped the handlebars.

We pedaled past row after row of one- and two-room plywood and cardboard shacks. We approached the Gomes's and saw Senhora Gomes standing in the middle of the street with a group of women. Her three small children played nearby.

"Senhora Gomes, *Feliz Natal*!" Sister Silva called out cheerfully.

Gomes stared at us, then grunted. Her friends stared.

"We missed you last Wednesday." Sister Silva gave her a big smile. We stopped our bikes, straddling them as we talked. "We came prepared with that special message about families."

Gomes's three children left their play and closed in, surrounding us.

"Ah, yes, Sisters, I'm so sorry," she said. "We were gone. It was an emergency. I had to go to my sister's house that morning . . ."

"But, *Mae*," her five-year-old daughter piped up, "when the sisters knocked, you made us hide under the table."

"*Cale a boca*, Maria!" The woman's words were sharp, mortified.

After an uncomfortable silence, Sister Silva said, "Well, we brought you a special message today. We know this message will make your Christmas Day extra special."

I glanced over at Sister Ribeiro. She looked back at me. She seemed to be holding her breath. There was mirth in her eyes, and her mouth was beginning to twitch.

Gomes folded her arms. "Sisters, to be honest, I'm not interested."

"That's all right," I said. "May we sing for you?"

"*Sing* for me?"

"A Christmas carol."

"I'm not interested."

"Senhora, Sister Ribeiro has cooked a Christmas treat for you and your children . . ."

"I said I'm not interested!"

"Okay, then. *Feliz Natal*, Senhora Gomes!"

We bicycled as quickly as we could down the road and around the corner. Sister Ribeiro still looked like she was about to explode. We reached the bridge, stopped our bikes, and burst out laughing. We couldn't help it. It was awful, laughing like that, but we couldn't contain it any longer.

"Now what?" Silva gasped.

"*Baixinho*!" Ribeiro exclaimed, as if she'd just had an epiphany. "The cake is for *Baixinho*."

Baixinho was the happiest man I'd ever known. Everything made him happy. His dirty one-room lean-to built out of concrete and plywood on a wall next to the alley made him happy. His dirty shorts and worn sandals were the only articles of clothing I'd ever seen him wear, and even that brought him joy. And when the sisters came to read to him because he'd never learned that skill for himself, his grin reached from one hair-tufted ear to the other. His colossal grin never wavered, and his white curly shock of hair stood out in stark contrast to the dark leathery skin of his face, upper torso, arms, and legs. He was at least seventy, and he claimed not to remember his real name. And yet, since everybody in his neighborhood called him *Baixinho*, or Shorty, not remembering didn't matter to him. Since his wide, smiling face came no higher than tiny Sister Ribeiro's armpits, the name fit him perfectly.

Baixinho was the cake's destination, and there couldn't have been a better one. Whatever the cake looked like after this afternoon's journey, Baixinho would be overjoyed to receive it.

He greeted us with open arms and lovingly received the broken, leprosy-inspired remains of Sister Ribeiro's chocolate cake. He grinned, sampled it, and then set it on the open windowsill. We sat in his tiny house and shared our Christmas message with him while he relaxed, with fingers laced across his leathery middle and his smile running from east to west.

While we sang "Silent Night" for him, we heard the cake disappear from his windowsill. Delinquent feet scurried away down the alley. Sister Ribeiro let out an incensed howl.

"Never mind," Baixinho smiled without moving from his seat. His hands remained laced together across his stomach. "It happens all the time."

"But it was your cake!"

Baixinho smiled all the wider and shrugged his bony shoulders. "They needed it more than me. Will you read some more from your book?"

So in only a moment, a tiny wrinkled man from Brazil taught me what really mattered most at Christmas. We read to him until *Praia Grande's* unique rhythm intensified, like drums pulsating through the heat, indicating the beginning of a night of revelry and Christmas debauchery. It was time for all good little missionaries to go home.

The sun set on this very unique, beautiful Brazilian Christmas Day, retiring behind us as we pedaled toward our apartment. I inhaled deeply the sweet ocean breeze and laughed out loud, feeling the warm wind moving my hair and Sister Ribeiro's earrings against my ears.

We had definitely found a *porpoise* for Christmas.

OTHER BOOKS BY SANDRA GREY

Traitor

Tribunal

Trespass

A VOICE FOR CHRISTMAS

BY SIAN ANN BESSEY

My first child, Jonathan, was born on June 25, 1985. He was delivered by emergency C-section after thirty-three hours of labor. Badly bruised and swollen, he was immediately whisked off to the NICU, where he was monitored for the first twenty-four hours of his life.

The unexpectedly difficult delivery also took its toll on me. When the surgery was over, no number of warm blankets could stop my shaking. I was in shock, and my body was struggling to cope. Over the next few hours, things continued to go downhill as further complications set in. I was placed on a liquid diet for five days, and by the time I was finally released from the hospital, I was weaker than I'd ever been in my life.

My recuperation was painfully slow, but over the next few weeks, my incision healed and my strength returned. Gradually, I resumed my former active lifestyle and was able to care for my infant son without experiencing pain with every movement. I rejoiced in every small accomplishment, from climbing the stairs unaided to pushing a vacuum across the room, but despite my body's remarkable recovery, I was unable to reclaim one thing—my voice.

From the time I'd left the surgery room, I'd been unable to raise my voice above a croaky whisper. Singing and shouting were impossible, and if I spoke for an extended length of time, I felt the strain in my throat. There seemed to be nothing I could do to improve the situation, and eventually I realized I needed to visit an ear, nose, and throat specialist to see if he could solve the mystery of my missing voice.

After listening to my medical history and checking my throat, the doctor surprised me by saying that he knew of other cases like mine.

"We still don't understand exactly what happens," he said, "but if a person experiences severe trauma, the nervous system can momentarily shut down. Even though it lasts for just a split second, everything within the nervous system's control then has to be retriggered. Sometimes something gets forgotten." He gave a regretful shrug. "In your case, it was your vocal chords. One has partial movement; the other is completely paralyzed."

I stared at him, trying to wrap my mind around this shocking diagnosis. "Will it ever work properly?" I asked in my raspy whisper.

He nodded. "Yes, but the only way to get it moving is to enter your vocal box surgically and use a specialized instrument to stimulate it into vibrating again."

Another surgery was pretty much last on my list of things to do, but I numbly listened as he explained the procedure and went over the costs. Apart from the fact that my body had only just recovered from a difficult surgery, my husband, Kent, and I were poor college students. We had minimal insurance. My recent hospital stay had already drained us financially, and I didn't know how we'd ever come up with the money for another operation.

I returned to our small apartment, anxious to tell Kent what I'd learned from the doctor, but he was in class, and I had no way of reaching him. So I did the next best thing: I called my mother. This was not as easy as it sounds. My family was in Wales, and there was a seven-hour time difference between us. Text messages, e-mail, instant messaging, Skype, and other methods of communicating that are so common now were nonexistent then. And on top of that, the cost of a trans-Atlantic phone call was astronomical.

We didn't talk long. My mother listened to the details of my visit to the doctor and shared her concern and sympathy. At the time, it didn't seem as though there was anything more she could do. But I was wrong. A couple of days later, she called me back.

"Sian, I've been in contact with an ENT specialist here," she said. "He agreed with your doctor's diagnosis, but he said he wouldn't do the surgery until you've gone six months with no sign of improvement."

I already knew the date six months from Jonathan's birthday. "That's Christmas Day," I told her.

"Yes," she said. "Dad and I have talked about it. You're still a British citizen. It would be cheaper to fly home and have the surgery done here for free than to pay to have it done in Utah." She paused. "How would you feel about coming home for Christmas?"

My heart started to pound. Attending a university half a world away from my family meant that it had been five years since I'd been with them for Christmas. If living with a paralyzed vocal chord for three more months gave me a Christmas in Wales with my family, I'd do it.

When Kent returned from his classes, he needed no persuading. Within a matter of weeks, our flights were booked and I was scheduled for a consultation and surgery at the hospital in North Wales. Jonathan and I were to leave at the beginning of December so I could have the operation before Christmas. Kent would stay in Utah long enough to take his finals, then fly out to join us.

* * *

Traveling during the winter is always risky, and on that particular December morning, my luck was out. A snow-storm followed by frigid temperatures had the airport de-icers moving from one plane to another in a frantic attempt to prevent the wholesale grounding of the Delta fleet. I sat in the plane, trying to entertain Jonathan as the de-icing spray hit the windows and time marched on. When we finally took off hours later than scheduled, I knew I was in trouble.

We landed at JFK in the middle of the night. I had my diaper bag packed before we touched down, and the moment the doors opened, I put the bag on one shoulder, Jonathan on my hip, and ran. By the time I arrived at the next terminal, my legs were on fire, and I was gasping for breath. But I was too late. The one remaining Delta official at the gate was standing at the locked terminal door, watching the jumbo jet pull away from the Jetway.

"Can you call it back?" I wheezed.

"I'm sorry, ma'am." She was completely no-nonsense. "Once the Jetway's pulled back, there's nothing we can do."

"But I have to be in London tomorrow morning," I said. "My father's already left North Wales to meet me there, and I have no way of contacting him."

The official gave me a look that said she'd heard similar stories before and wasn't remotely interested in mine.

"You'll have to talk to someone at the Delta desk," she said, pointing down the terminal. "Ground floor."

By now the airplane's blinking lights were fading into the distance, but I wasn't going to give up. Hiking Jonathan higher onto my hip, I hurried off in search of the Delta desk.

There were two people working there, and the young man beckoned me forward.

"I just arrived on the Delta flight from Salt Lake City," I explained, "but I missed my connection to London. I have to get there tomorrow morning."

He extended his hand for my ticket and started clicking through screens on his computer.

"We can put you on the next Delta flight into London," he said, "but it doesn't leave until 10:30 a.m."

This man obviously didn't understand that staying in the JFK airport all night with a six-month-old was *not* an option. "I'm sorry," I said. My throat ached from the strain I was putting on my vocal chords, but I was determined to stay firm. "I don't have enough diapers for my baby to stay here that long. I need you to find me another flight that leaves this evening."

He must have never heard that argument before because he seemed momentarily nonplussed.

And in that moment of hesitation, the older lady who'd been working beside him swooped in to the rescue. "One minute," she said, picking up her phone and dialing a number.

She spoke to someone, nodded a few times, then hung up.

"PanAm has a flight leaving in ten minutes," she said. "They'll hold the door if you can get there right away."

"Where do I go?" I asked.

The young man pointed behind me. "You'll have to go out those doors, take a left and walk until you reach the signs for the train, then—"

The older woman gave him a withering look. "This lady's taking a taxi," she said. "And you're calling it for her."

I wanted to hug her, but with an airplane waiting and my arms full of a baby and diaper bag, all I could do was race for the door with a heartfelt thank-you.

* * *

A PanAm stewardess was standing at the gate, watching for me.

"Please," I gasped, glancing at the pay phones on the wall a few yards from the entry to the Jetway. "I need to make a phone call. No one knows that I'm coming in on this flight."

The stewardess glanced at her watch and frowned. "I can only give you two minutes."

That was all I needed. I ran to the nearest booth and sat down. With Jonathan on my knee, I placed a collect call to Kent.

"I can only speak for one minute," I said the moment the call connected. "I need you to call Mum and tell her we missed our connection in New York. We'll be flying into London on a PanAm flight scheduled to land in Heathrow at ten past eleven in the morning. She needs to call Heathrow and have Dad paged so he knows where to find me."

"Are you both okay?" Kent asked. I could hear the worry in his voice.

"Yes," I croaked. "Jonathan's been so good. But I have to go now; they're holding the flight for me. I'll let you know once we arrive home. Call Mum as soon as you can."

"I will," he said. "Be safe. I love you." And then he was gone.

Jonathan and I boarded the flight and collapsed into our seat as the airplane pulled away from the terminal.

Six and a half hours later, we landed in London. We had no luggage (I had absolutely no idea where it had ended up), but we were safely on British soil. The airport was bedecked with Christmas decorations and familiar signs for places and products I hadn't seen in years, but I had eyes for only one person. And as soon as I exited customs and immigration, I spotted him. By a series of miracles, Kent and my mother had managed to make contact with my father, and there he was, moving out of the waiting crowd toward us.

"You made it!" he said, wrapping his arms around me.

With my one free hand, I returned his squeeze. I'd waited a long time for this. Then as Jonathan started squirming, I pulled back and introduced my son to his grandfather for the first time. Dad held out his arms, but Jonathan buried his face in my shoulder. He'd already experienced too many unfamiliar things for one day.

"All right." Dad chuckled. "You keep Jonathan. I'll take the luggage."

I grimaced. "All I have is the diaper bag. I've reported my missing suitcase to the man at the lost luggage office, and he said they'd send it up on the train as soon as they've located it."

"Well, that's all we can do," Dad said. "Let's go home."

Travel weary and jet-lagged, Jonathan slept for most of the seven-hour drive. I dozed. Dad was our hero. Even though he'd spent the previous night in the car, he drove all the way, and we arrived home to a wonderful welcome. Christmas decorations hung on the walls, a tree twinkled in the living room, greeting cards covered every surface, but best of all, my whole family was there. For me, it was a tender reunion. For Jonathan, it was his first opportunity to meet my five younger siblings and become reacquainted with his grandmother, who hadn't seen him since he was one week old.

As soon as my mother learned about our lost luggage, she brought out Jonathan's Christmas presents, and we opened them right then and there. Within minutes, he had a pair of warm pajamas and another outfit to wear while we washed the clothes he'd traveled in. With a package of diapers and wipes already waiting for us in my bedroom, we had everything we needed.

The next day I woke early for my appointment with the ENT doctor. I was just about to leave for the hospital when my mother pulled me aside.

"I called the London temple yesterday," she said. "I asked them to put your name on the temple roll. I felt that you might need a few extra prayers to help you make it through your long journey and all you have ahead with your throat."

I stared at her, not sure if my throat was aching from strain or from unshed tears. I'd spent the last six months living within walking distance of the Provo temple, and not once had I considered the power of the temple prayer roll. Just as had happened so many times in my youth, my mother's example of living by faith lifted me and filled me with hope and gratitude. It was impossible to look back on my recent trip and not recognize the divine help Jonathan and I had received.

Was it possible that the prayers coming from the temple would continue to bless me? Could they extend to helping with my medical condition? A feeling of comfort enveloped me, and I gave my mother a hug. Whatever lay ahead, I felt assured that things would be all right.

The hospital had made a mediocre attempt at decorating the waiting room. A small bedraggled Christmas tree stood on the counter, and a handful of Christmas cards had been attached to the pin board, adding a splash of color to the otherwise boring medical notices.

A nurse called my name, and I followed her out of the waiting room and into a small examining room. Soon afterward, a doctor walked in. He sat on a stool opposite me and listened as I told him about my throat. He nodded a few times, then he picked up a tongue depressor.

"Open," he said.

I complied, and he sprayed something down my throat and shone a bright light into the back of my mouth.

"Repeat these sounds," he said, rattling off a series of vowels and consonants.

My throat ached, but I made the sounds. He gave a satisfied nod and clicked off the light.

"One vocal chord is vibrating properly," he said. "The other is functioning at about 70 percent efficiency. You should be back to normal very soon."

"You mean . . ." I had to be clear on what he was telling me. "You mean I don't need to have surgery?"

"That's right," he said. "The way things look now, I'd guess both vocal chords will be working properly within about a week."

The doctor could not have known how his matter-of-fact diagnosis fanned the little flame of faith my mother had lit that morning. I put my hand on my throat. In the last forty-eight hours, I'd strained my vocal chords more than ever before. I'd been forced to talk through the complications of a missed connection, explain my lack of luggage to customs officials, apologize to immigration officers for taking my American-born son through the British-passports-only line, and make arrangements for the delivery of my lost luggage. And all that time, patrons of the London temple had been praying for me. The thought was both edifying and humbling.

"Thank you," I managed, coming to my feet.

"You're welcome," the doctor said, shaking my hand. "Have a happy Christmas."

* * *

Ten days later, I was with my family, participating in our annual Christmas Eve program. Kent had arrived safely and was seated beside me. Jonathan was being passed from one aunt's arms to the next. My luggage full of Christmas gifts had been found and delivered, and rather than spending a week in the hospital recovering from surgery, I'd spent it sharing favorite Christmas traditions with my family in Wales. I was full of gratitude.

As my father finished reading the story of the Savior's birth from the Bible, my family began to sing "The First Noel," and for the first time in six months, I sang too. I made it through the entire first verse before stopping to rest my newly functioning vocal chords.

My mother turned my way and smiled. Joy filled my heart. Christmas was a time of miracles. And this year, along with the miracle of the Savior's birth, I'd been given a Christmas miracle of my own.

OTHER BOOKS BY SIAN ANN BESSEY

Uprising in Samoa

Ambushed in Africa

Escape from Germany

A Family Is Forever

Cover of Darkness

Deception

The Insider

You Came for Me

Within the Dark Hills

One Last Spring

To Win a Lady's Heart